CARNEGIE LEARNING

LONG + LIVE + MATH

Middle School
Math Solution
Course 3

Student Edition
Volume 2

Sandy Bartle Finocchi and Amy Jones Lewis
with Kelly Edenfield and Josh Fisher

CARNEGIE LEARNING

501 Grant St., Suite 1075
Pittsburgh, PA 15219
Phone 888.851.7094
Customer Service Phone 412.690.2444
Fax 412.690.2444

www.carnegielearning.com

Cover Design by Anne Milliron

ISBN: 978-1-68459-289-0
Student Edition, Volume 2

Printed in the United States of America

3 4 5 6 7 8 9 BB 21

LONG + LIVE + MATH

Acknowledgments

Middle School Math Solution Authors

- Sandy Bartle Finocchi, Senior Academic Officer
- Amy Jones Lewis, Director of Instructional Design
- Kelly Edenfield, Instructional Designer
- Josh Fisher, Instructional Designer

Foundation Authors (2010)

- William S. Hadley, Algebra and Proportional Reasoning
- Mary Lou Metz, Data Analysis and Probability
- Mary Lynn Raith, Number and Operations
- Janet Sinopoli, Algebra
- Jaclyn Snyder, Geometry and Measurement

Vendors

- Lumina Datamatics, Ltd.
- Cenveo Publisher Services, Inc.

Images

- www.pixabay.com

Special Thanks

- Alison Huettner for project management and editorial review.
- Jacyln Snyder and Janet Sinopoli for their contributions to the Teacher's Implementation Guide facilitation notes.
- Victoria Fisher for her review of content and contributions to all the ancillary materials.
- Valerie Muller for her contributions and review of content.
- The members of Carnegie Learning's Cognitive Scientist Team—Brendon Towle, John Connelly, Bob Hausmann, Chas Murray, and Martina Pavelko—for their insight in learning science and review of content.
- Bob Hausmann for his contributions to the Family Guide.
- John Jorgenson, Chief Marketing Officer, for all his insight and messaging.
- Carnegie Learning's Education Services Team for content review and providing customer feedback.
- In Memory of David Dengler, Director of Curriculum Development (Deceased), who made substantial contributions to conceptualizing Carnegie Learning's middle school software.

"Mathematics is so much more than memorizing rules. It is learning to reason, to make connections, and to make sense of the world. We believe in Learning by Doing™—you need to actively engage with the content if you are to benefit from it. The lessons were designed to take you from your intuitive understanding of the world and build on your prior experiences to then learn new concepts. My hope is that these instructional materials help you build a deep understanding of math.

Sandy Bartle Finocchi, Senior Academic Officer

"My hope is that as you work through this course, you feel capable—capable of exploring new ideas that build upon what you already know, capable of struggling through challenging problems, capable of thinking creatively about how to fix mistakes, and capable of thinking like a mathematician.

Amy Jones Lewis, Director of Instructional Design

"At Carnegie Learning we have created an organization whose mission and culture is defined by your success. Our passion is creating products that make sense of the world of mathematics and ignite a passion in you. Our hope is that you will enjoy our resources as much as we enjoyed creating them.

Barry Malkin, CEO

Table of Contents

Module 1: Transforming Geometric Objects

Module 2: Developing Function Foundations

Topic 1: From Proportions to Linear Relationships

Topic 2: Linear Relationships

Topic 3: Introduction to Functions

Topic 4: Patterns in Bivariate Data

Module 3: Modeling Linear Equations

Topic 1: Solving Linear Equations

Topic 2: Systems of Linear Equations

Module 4: Expanding Number Systems

Topic 1: The Real Number System

Module 5: Applying Powers

MODULE 3

MODELING

LINEAR EQUATIONS

The lessons in this module build on your experiences of solving two-step equations and graphing linear equations. You will apply number properties as strategies to write equations in equivalent forms and explore strategies for solving equations with variables on both sides of the equals sign. You will write and solve equations to answer questions about real-world situations. You will also use systems of linear equations to solve real-world problems.

TOPIC 1
Solving Linear Equations

The game of Bingo dates back to 16th century Italy. The modern version of the game was copyrighted by Hugh Ward of Pittsburgh, Pennsylvania, in 1924.

Module 3: Modeling Linear Equations

TOPIC 1: SOLVING LINEAR EQUATIONS

In this topic, students increase the range of one-variable linear equations they can solve. Students solve equations with variables on both sides of the equals sign. They review and learn strategies, including the use of properties of arithmetic, to efficiently solve equations with rational number coefficients. Students develop an understanding of the conditions that lead to equations with one solution, no solution, or infinite solutions.

Where have we been?

In grade 7, students have solved equations of the form $px + q = r$ and $p(x + q) = r$, where p, q, and r are rational numbers. They have also used properties, including the Distributive Property, to factor and expand algebraic expressions. Now, just as they did in grade 7, students review and/ or learn strategies in this topic to make solving such equations more efficient.

Where are we going?

This topic provides the bridge from solving one-variable equations with variables on one side of the equals sign to solving systems of linear equations algebraically. Solving equations with no solution or with infinite solutions also prepares students to solve, algebraically, systems of linear equations with no solution or infinite solutions.

Using the Properties of Equality to Solve Equations

Students have been using these Properties of Equality throughout elementary and middle school. Understanding these properties allows students to understand much of the logic behind solving equations.

Properties of Equality	For all numbers a, b, and c, ...
Addition Property of Equality	If $a = b$, then $a + c = b + c$.
Subtraction Property of Equality	If $a = b$, then $a - c = b - c$.
Multiplication Property of Equality	If $a = b$, then $ac = bc$.
Division Property of Equality	If $a = b$ and $c \neq 0$, then $\frac{a}{c} = \frac{b}{c}$.

Myth: "Just give me the rule. If I know the rule, then I understand the math."

Memorize the following rule: *All quars are elos*. Will you remember that rule tomorrow? Nope. Why not? Because it has no meaning. It isn't connected to anything you know. What if we change the rule to: *All squares are parallelograms*. How about now? Can you remember that? Of course you can, because now it makes sense.

Learning does not take place in a vacuum. It **must be** connected to what you already know. Otherwise, arbitrary rules will be forgotten.

#mathmythbusted

Talking Points

You can further support your student's learning by making sure they eat right and get enough sleep. Healthy bodies make for healthy minds, and both diet and sleep have significant effects on learning.

Key Terms

no solutions

An equation may have no solutions. The equation $x = x + 2$, for example, has no solutions. No value of x can make the equation true.

one solution

An equation may have one solution. The equation $8 = x + 2$, for example, has one solution. The value $x = 6$ makes the equation true.

infinite solutions

An equation may have an infinite number of solutions. The equation $x(1 + 1) = 2x$, for example, has infinite solutions. An infinite number of values for x make the equation true.

Strategic Solving

Equations with Variables on Both Sides

WARM UP

Solve each equation.

1. $2.5x + 100 = 600$

2. $10 = 2x - 4$

3. $\frac{1}{4}x + 5 = 30$

LEARNING GOALS

- Use strategies to solve linear equations with variables on both sides of the equals sign.
- Solve linear equations with rational number coefficients.
- Combine like terms and use the Distributive Property to solve linear equations.

You have solved equations by combining like terms and using inverse operations. How can you solve equations when there are variables on both sides of the equation?

Build It Up and Break It Down

The Properties of Equality allow you to solve equations.

Properties of Equality	For all numbers a, b, and c
Addition Property of Equality	If $a = b$, then $a + c = b + c$.
Subtraction Property of Equality	If $a = b$, then $a - c = b - c$.
Multiplication Property of Equality	If $a = b$, then $ac = bc$.
Division Property of Equality	If $a = b$ and $c \neq 0$, then $\frac{a}{c} = \frac{b}{c}$.

These properties also allow you to create more complex equations. For example, given the equation $x = 2$, you can use the Addition Property of Equality to create $x + 1 = 2 + 1$, which is the same as $x + 1 = 3$. Since you used the Properties of Equality, the two equations have the same solution.

To solve a two-step equation, isolate the variable term on one side of the equation and the constant on the other side of the equation. Then multiply or divide both sides of the equation by the numeric coefficient to determine the value of the variable.

1. **Consider each given equation. Use the Properties of Equality to create an equivalent equation in the form $ax + b = c$, where a, b, and c can be any number. Record the Properties of Equality you used to create your new equation.**

   a. $x = 5$ b. $x = -1$

2. **Give each of your equations to a partner to verify that each equation has the correct solution.**

Factoring to Solve Equations

You have previously solved two-step equations using a variety of strategies. In this activity you will learn different strategies to solve equations with variables on both sides. Remember, to solve an equation means to determine the value of the unknown that makes the equation true.

Consider the equation $5x + 3 = 2x + 5$.

Teddy and Topher each solved it in a different way. Analyze their solution strategies.

To begin solving an equation with variables on both sides of the equation, move all the variable terms to one side of the equation and all the constants to the other side of the equation.

Teddy 👍

$$5x + 3 = 2x + 5$$
$$-5x \qquad -5x$$
$$\overline{\qquad \qquad}$$
$$3 = -3x + 5$$
$$-5 \qquad -5$$
$$\overline{\qquad \qquad}$$
$$\frac{-2}{-3} = \frac{-3x}{-3}$$
$$\frac{2}{3} = x$$
$$x = \frac{2}{3}$$

Topher 👍

$$5x + 3 = 2x + 5$$
$$-2x \qquad -2x$$
$$\overline{\qquad \qquad}$$
$$3x + 3 = \qquad 5$$
$$-3 \qquad -3$$
$$\overline{\qquad \qquad}$$
$$3x = 2$$
$$x = \frac{2}{3}$$

1. Compare the two solution strategies.

   a. How were their solution strategies the same? How were they different?

   b. Which strategy do you prefer? Explain your choice.

2. Solve each equation. Describe why you chose your solution strategy.

   a. $x - 6 = 5x + 10$ b. $2x - 7 = -5x + 14$

Consider the two different equations that Sandy and Sara solved.

NOTES

Sandy

$3x + 9 = 6x - 30$

$\dfrac{3x + 9}{3} = \dfrac{6x - 30}{3}$

$x + 3 = 2x - 10$

$\underline{-x \qquad\quad -x}$

$3 = x - 10$

$\underline{+10 \qquad\quad +10}$

$13 = x$

$x = 13$

Sara

$-x - 2 = -4x - 1$

$\dfrac{-x - 2}{-1} = \dfrac{-4x - 1}{-1}$

$x + 2 = 4x + 1$

$\underline{-x \qquad\quad -x}$

$2 = 3x + 1$

$\underline{-1 \qquad\quad - 1}$

$1 = 3x$

$\dfrac{1}{3} = \dfrac{3x}{3}$

$\dfrac{1}{3} = x$

$x = \dfrac{1}{3}$

3. Sandy and Sara each divided both sides of their equations by a factor and then solved.

   a. Explain the reasoning used by each.

   b. Do you think this solution strategy will work for any equation? Explain your reasoning.

4. Solve each equation using the strategy similar to Sandy and Sara.

   a. $-4x + 8 = 2x + 10$ b. $-42x = -4x - 1$

ACTIVITY 1.2 Solving Equations with Efficiency

As you saw in the last activity, there can be more than one way to solve an equation. Sometimes an efficient strategy involves changing the numbers in the equation—in mathematically appropriate ways.

A savvy mathematician (you!) can look at an equation, see the structure of the equation, and look for the most efficient solution strategy.

> **WORKED EXAMPLE**
>
> Consider the equation $\frac{1}{3}(2x + 7) + \frac{5}{6} = \frac{5}{3}x$.
>
> You can multiply both sides of the equation by the least common denominator (LCD) of the fractions to convert the fractions to whole numbers.
>
> $\frac{1}{3}(2x + 7) + \frac{5}{6} = \frac{5}{3}x$ ← The LCD of the fractions is 6. Multiply both sides by 6.
>
> $2(2x + 7) + 5 = 10x$ ← Rewrite using the Distributive Property.
> $4x + 14 + 5 = 10x$

1. **Explain how both sides of the equation were multiplied by 6 in the first step.**

2. **What is the solution to the equation $\frac{1}{3}(2x + 7) + \frac{5}{6} = \frac{5}{3}x$? Check your solution.**

3. Explain why Cody's reasoning is incorrect.

> ## Cody
>
> $-\frac{3}{4}x = \frac{1}{2}x + \frac{5}{4}$
>
> $4\left(-\frac{3}{4}x\right) = 4\left(\frac{1}{2}x + \frac{5}{4}\right)$
>
> $-3x = 2x + 5$
>
> $-5x = 5$
>
> $x = -1$
>
> Since I multiplied both sides by 4 to get the solution, I have to divide the solution by 4:
>
> $x = -\frac{1}{4}$

4. Solve each equation by first multiplying both sides of the equation by the LCD. Check your solutions.

   a. $\frac{1}{4}(x - 5) + 9 = \frac{1}{2}x$ b. $\frac{5}{4}\left(x + \frac{1}{2}\right) + 8 = \frac{1}{8}x$

5. Mindy and David multiplied both sides of the equation $2.5x + 1.4 = 0.5x + 2$ by 10 before solving the equation. The first step of each strategy is shown. Who's correct? What is the error in the other strategy?

> ## Mindy
>
> $25x + 14 = 5x + 2$

> ## David
>
> $25x + 14 = 5x + 20$

You can multiply both sides of an equation by powers of 10 to convert all numbers to whole numbers.

ACTIVITY 1.3

Practice Solving Equations

NOTES

Solve each equation.

1. $12.6 + 4x = 9.6 + 8x$

2. $-12.11x - 10.5 = 75.6 - 3.5x$

3. $\dfrac{10x + 2}{2} = 4x + \dfrac{1}{4}$

4. $\dfrac{3}{8}(x + 8) = \dfrac{1}{2}(x + 5) + \dfrac{1}{4}$

5. $\dfrac{-2(5x + 4)}{3} = -3(3x + 2) - \dfrac{7}{3}$

TALK the TALK 💬

Building Strategically

Use each starting equation to build an equation with variables on both sides that can be solved using the given strategy. Then, give your equations to a partner to solve.

1. $h = 1.6$, factor out a number from both sides

2. $j = 5$, multiply both sides by the LCD to rewrite fractions as whole numbers

3. $k = \frac{1}{3}$, multiply both sides by a power of 10 to rewrite decimals as whole numbers

Assignment

Write

Explain the process of solving an equation with variables on both sides.

Remember

You can use Properties of Equality to rewrite equations and increase your efficiency with solving equations.

- Factor out a number from both sides.
- Multiply both sides of an equation by the least common denominator of the fractions to rewrite fractions as whole numbers.
- Multiply both sides of an equation by a power of 10 to rewrite decimals as whole numbers.
- Use the Distributive Property to rewrite expressions.

Practice

Solve each equation.

1. $5x + 15 = 75 - 25x$

2. $\frac{1}{4}x - 3 = \frac{1}{2}x + 12$

3. $4x = 20x - 24$

4. $11.3x + 12.8 = 7.5x + 35.6$

5. $9.6x - 15.4 = -4.3x + 26.3$

6. $-2x - 1.4 = 6 + 3x$

Stretch

You can solve an equation with two variables by trying different values. What is the solution to the equation $2x + 3y = 13$?

Review

1. Rodell took a survey of his classmates. The data from the survey are shown in the two-way table.

Student's Lunch Preference

		Lunch Options				
		Chicken Nuggets	Peanut Butter & Jelly	Pizza	Salad	Total
Gender	Male	2	3	4	0	9
	Female	3	1	3	4	11
	Total	5	4	7	4	20

a. Which lunch option is the most favorite of the males?

b. Which lunch option is the most favorite of the females?

2. Isabel surveyed three classes about their favorite season. The data from the survey are shown in the two-way table. Complete the relative frequencies for each row. If necessary, round decimals to the nearest thousandth.

Student's Season Preference

		Seasons				
		Winter	Spring	Summer	Fall	Total
Classes	Class A	9	2	7	6	24
	Class B	2	5	9	4	20
	Class C	8	6	10	4	28
	Total	19	13	26	14	72

Student's Season Preference

		Seasons				
		Winter	Spring	Summer	Fall	Total
Classes	Class A	$\frac{9}{24} = 0.375$				
	Class B					
	Class C					

3. Calculate the slope of the line represented by each table.

a.

X	Y
4	8
10	11
16	14
20	16

b.

X	Y
2	5
4	3
5	2
8	−1

MP3s and DVDs

2

Analyzing and Solving Linear Equations

WARM UP

Members of a community service club are collecting pull tabs from aluminum cans to support a local hospital's initiative.

- Sadie collected the least number of pull tabs.
- Emma collected 15 more pull tabs than Sadie.
- Ricky collected 4 times as many as Emma.
- Lily collected 10 fewer than Ricky.

Define a variable to represent the number of pull tabs that Sadie collected. Then, write algebraic expressions to represent the number of pull tabs that each of the other students collected.

LEARNING GOALS

- Write and solve linear equations in one variable.
- Determine whether an equation has one solution, no solutions, or infinite solutions by successively transforming the equation into simpler forms.
- Interpret expressions in and solutions to equations in the context of problem situations.

You have learned how to use strategies to solve complex equations with variables on both sides. How can you determine when an equation has no solutions or infinite solutions?

No One Knows Exactly

Sometimes, you are asked to determine the value of unknown quantities using only information you have for a quantity.

Five friends have a certain number of DVDs.

- Dan has the fewest.

- Donna has 7 more than Dan.

- Betty has twice as many as Donna.

- Jerry has 3 times as many as Dan.

- Kenesha has 6 fewer than Donna.

1. Define a variable for the number of DVDs that Dan has.

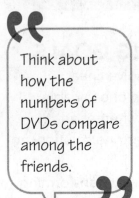

Think about how the numbers of DVDs compare among the friends.

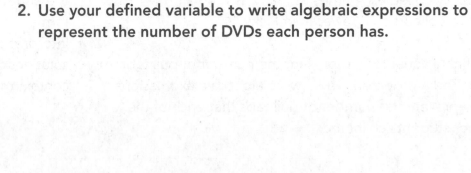

2. Use your defined variable to write algebraic expressions to represent the number of DVDs each person has.

Writing Expressions to Represent Situations

Use the expressions you wrote in the previous activity to answer each question.

1. Is it possible for Jerry and Kenesha to have an equal number of DVDs? Write and solve an algebraic equation to explain why or why not.

2. Kim and Corinne share their own set of DVDs. Kim has 6 times as many as Dan has, and Corinne has twice as many as Jerry has. Can you write and solve an equation to determine how many DVDs each girl has? Explain your reasoning.

3. If the original group of friends has a total of 182 DVDs all together, then how many does each person have? Make sure to check your work.

   a. DVDs that Dan owns: b. DVDs that Donna owns:

   c. DVDs that Betty owns: d. DVDs that Jerry owns:

   e. DVDs that Kenesha owns:

4. Write and solve an algebraic equation to show why Donna's reasoning is incorrect.

Donna

Donna says that the sum of the number of her DVDs and Kenesha's DVDs is the same as the number of DVDs that Betty owns.

Terry, Trudy, Tom, and Trevor have challenged their friends with
this riddle.

• Terry said, "If you add 150 to the number of MP3 downloads Tom
  has, double that number, and finally divide by 3, you have the
  number of MP3 downloads I have."

• Trudy said, "If you take the number of MP3 downloads Tom has,
  subtract 30, multiply that difference by 5, and finally divide that
  product by 4, the result will be the number of MP3 downloads I
  have."

• Trevor said, "Well, if you take twice the number of MP3
  downloads Tom has, add 30, multiply the sum by 4, and finally
  divide that product by 3, you will have the number of MP3
  downloads I have."

1. **What do you need to know to determine the number of MP3
   downloads each person has?**

2. **Define a variable for the number of MP3 downloads Tom has,
   and then write expressions for the number of MP3 downloads
   each of the other people has.**

   a. **The number of MP3 downloads Terry has:**

   b. **The number of MP3 downloads Trudy has:**

   c. **The number of MP3 downloads Trevor has:**

3. Suppose Tom has 150 MP3 downloads. Determine how many MP3 downloads each person has.

Terry   Trudy   Trevor

4. What if Terry and Trevor have the same number of MP3 downloads? How many MP3 downloads would each person have?

Tom   Trudy   Trevor and Terry

5. What if the sum of Trudy's and Trevor's MP3 downloads is 39 more than the number Terry has? How many would each person have?

Tom   Trudy

Trevor   Terry

Amy and Damon were solving an equation from their math homework. They came across the equation shown.

$$3x + 7 = 5x + 2(3 - x) + 1$$

Examine each solution strategy.

Amy

$$3x + 7 = 5x + 2(3 - x) + 1$$
$$3x - 5x + 7 = 5x - 5x + 2(3 - x) + 1$$
$$-2x + 7 = 2(3 - x) + 1$$
$$-2x + 7 = 6 + (-2x) + 1$$
$$-2x + 7 = 7 + (-2x)$$
$$-2x + 2x + 7 = 7 + (-2x) + 2x$$
$$7 = 7$$

What did Damon do differently to solve the equation?

Damon

$$3x + 7 = 5x + 2(3 - x) + 1$$
$$3x + 7 = 5x + 6 + (-2x) + 1$$
$$3x + 7 = 5x + (-2x) + 6 + 1$$
$$3x + 7 = 3x + 7$$
$$3x + 7 + (-7) = 3x + 7 + (-7)$$
$$\frac{3x}{3} = \frac{3x}{3}$$
$$x = x$$

1. Explain why both Amy's and Damon's methods are correct but have different solutions.

2. How would you interpret the final equation in each solution? Is the final equation always true, sometimes true, or never true? Explain your reasoning.

3. Explain whether the equation has one solution, no solution, or an infinite number of solutions.

What happened to the term with the variable?

Consider this new equation:

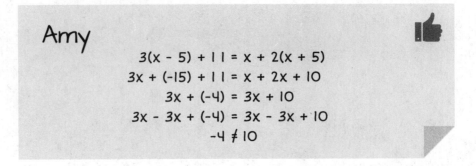

$$3(x - 5) + 11 = x + 2(x + 5)$$

Examine each solution strategy.

Amy 👍

$$3(x - 5) + 11 = x + 2(x + 5)$$
$$3x + (-15) + 11 = x + 2x + 10$$
$$3x + (-4) = 3x + 10$$
$$3x - 3x + (-4) = 3x - 3x + 10$$
$$-4 \neq 10$$

Damon 👍

$$3(x - 5) + 11 = x + 2(x + 5)$$
$$3x + (-15) + 11 = x + 2x + 10$$
$$3x + (-4) + 4 = 3x + 10 + 4$$
$$3x = 3x + 14$$
$$3x + (-3x) = 3x + (-3x) + 14$$
$$0 \neq 14$$

4. Explain why both Amy's and Damon's methods are correct but have different solutions.

5. How would you interpret the final equation in each solution? Is the final equation always true, sometimes true, or never true? Explain your reasoning.

6. Explain whether the equation has one solution, no solution, or an infinite number of solutions.

Solve each equation shown. Make sure to check your work.

1. $\frac{3}{4}(2x + 5) = 14$

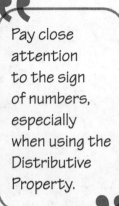

Pay close attention to the sign of numbers, especially when using the Distributive Property.

2. $2x - 7 + 3x = 4x + 2$

3. $\frac{-7(3x + 6)}{3} = 7$

4. $1.99x + 6 = 2.50x$

5. $40x = -50(x - 2)$

6. $30(x - 10) = 15x$

7. $3(x - 1) + x = 4(x + 2)$

8. $5(2x - 1) + x + 17 = 5x + 6(x + 2)$

9. $\frac{-3(-2x - 5)}{4} = -5(3x + 5) + \frac{5}{4}$

10. $\frac{2}{3}(6x - 5) = 2 - \frac{1}{3}(3x - 2)$

TALK the TALK 💬

How Do You Know?

1. When you solve any equation, describe how you know when there will be:

   a. one solution.

   b. no solutions.

   c. infinite solutions.

Assignment

Write

Write three equations, one that has one solution, one that has no solutions, and one that has infinite solutions.

Remember

An equation can have one solution, no solutions, or infinite solutions.

Practice

1. Don has four different chicken coops on his farm. He gathers eggs from each coop every day to sell at the local farmer's market each week. During one week in the summer, the production levels from the coops were compared.

   - The number of eggs from coop B can be found by subtracting 10 from coop A's production, and then multiplying this result by two-fifths.
   - The number of eggs from coop C can be found by adding 3 to coop A's production, multiplying this amount by 3, subtracting 4 from this total, and then dividing the whole result by 4.
   - The number of eggs from coop D can be found by adding 7 to coop A's production, doubling this amount and then dividing the result by 3.

   a. Define a variable for the number of eggs produced by coop A. Then write expressions for the number of eggs produced by the other coops.

   b. If coop A produced 125 eggs, how many did each of the other coops produce?

   c. If the sum of the number of eggs from coop B and coop C was 24 more than the number of eggs from coop D, how many eggs did each coop produce?

2. Three siblings collect rare coins. To determine the number of rare coins that Samantha has, take the number of rare coins Kevin has, add 4, and then divide that sum by 2. To determine the number of rare coins Ben has, double the number of rare coins Kevin has, subtract 4, and then multiply that difference by 2. How many rare coins does each sibling have if they have a total of 49 rare coins?

3. Three teammates had different point totals at the girls' basketball game. To determine the number of points Effie had, multiply Toni's points by 3, subtract 8, and then multiply the difference by 2. To determine the number of points Linda had, add 9 to Toni's points and divide the sum by 3. How many points did each girl have if Effie scored 9 more than Toni and Linda combined?

4. Four members of the track team ran various numbers of miles last week. To determine the number of miles Manuel ran, multiply the number of miles Ewan ran by 3, subtract 15, multiply the difference by 2, and divide this quantity by 5. To determine the number of miles Violet ran, subtract 14 from the number of miles Ewan ran, and then multiply the difference by 3. To determine the number of miles Ling ran, add 30 to the number of miles Ewan ran, and then divide the sum by 5. How many miles did each team member run last week if the total number of miles run by Ewan and Manuel is equal to the total number of miles run by Violet and Ling?

Stretch

When an equation is not a linear equation, it can have more than one solution. The equation $x^2 = 9$ has two solutions, -3 and 3. What are the solutions to the equation $2x^2 + 5 = 77$?

Review

Solve each equation.

1. $\frac{2}{3}(x + 2) = \frac{1}{6}x + \frac{1}{3}$
2. $2.5x - 1 = 10 - 7.5x$

Determine whether there is likely a positive or negative association between the quantities.
Explain your reasoning.

3. Independent quantity: number of sunny days in Year A

   Dependent quantity: number of cloudy days in Year A

4. Independent quantity: number of miles driven

   Dependent quantity: amount of gas in tank

Determine the slope and y-intercept of the line represented by each equation.

5. $36 = 24y + 48x$
6. $y - 14 = 7x + 9$

Tic-Tac-Bingo

Creating Linear Equations

WARM UP

Solve each equation.

1. $\frac{2}{3}(x - 4) = \frac{1}{2}$

2. $0.7(x + 3) = 2.1$

3. $3(-2x + 5) = 5x - 7$

4. $\frac{3x + 11}{2} = x - 4$

LEARNING GOALS

- Solve linear equations with rational coefficients and variables on both sides.
- Give examples of linear equations with one solution, no solutions, or infinite solutions.
- Determine whether an equation has one solution, no solutions, or infinite solutions.

You know how to solve linear equations and determine the number of solutions. How can you create linear equations with zero, one, or infinite solutions?

The Goal

In this lesson, each person in the class will be given a different algebraic expression. Your goal is to locate a classmate and form an equation to meet each of the criteria listed.

    a. no solution

    b. a non-zero integer solution

    c. a negative rational solution

    d. a positive rational solution

    e. a solution that is neither positive nor negative

    f. infinite solutions

1. **For each criterion, provide an example of a final line of the solved equation.**

Use the Tic-Tac-Bingo board at the end of the lesson. The board has 9 spaces. Three spaces are already designated.

1. Fill each remaining space with one of the solution types listed. Each option must be used at least once.

   - **positive rational solution**

   - **negative rational solution**

   - **non-zero integer solution**

> Each equation can only be used in one box, but you can rearrange your equations if you need to.

2. Your teacher will assign your expression. When you and a classmate have created an equation with one of the solution types, write your equation in the corresponding box.

Try to be the first person to get three in a row. Then, try to be the first person to completely fill your board with equations.

TALK the TALK

The Strategy

Think about the strategies you used to play Tic-Tac-Bingo.

1. **Describe your general strategy.**

2. **Reflect on the equations with no solutions and infinite solutions.**

    a. **How can you look at an equation and determine that there will be no solution?**

    b. **How can you look at an equation and determine that there will be infinite solutions?**

Tic-Tac-Bingo

	Solution is not positive or negative	
Equation: **Solution:**	**Equation:** **Solution:**	**Equation:** **Solution:**
No Solution **Equation:**	FREE SPACE	**Equation:** **Solution:**
Equation: **Solution:**	**Equation:** **Solution:**	Infinite Solutions **Equation:**

Assignment

Write

Explain the difference between an equation with no solution and an equation with a solution of $x = 0$.

Remember

Linear equations can have no solution, one solution, or infinite solutions.

Practice

1. Set each given expression equal to $7(x - 2) - 4x + 14$. Determine whether the equation formed has no solution, infinite solutions, or a solution of $x = 0$.

   a. no solution $\frac{8x + 4}{2} - \frac{1}{3}(x + 6)$

   b. infinite solutions $2(x - 1) + x$

   c. solution of $x = 0$ $-9x + 12 + 4(3x - 3)$

2. Set each given expression equal to $\frac{7}{3}x + 4 - \frac{x - 6}{3}$. Determine whether the equation formed has no solution, infinite solutions, or a solution of $x = 0$.

   a. no solution $\frac{1}{3}(8x + 18) - \frac{2}{3}x$

   b. infinite solutions $2(3x + 5) - 4$

   c. solution of $x = 0$ $4\left(\frac{1}{2}x - 3\right) + 6$

Stretch

Create an equation with at least one fractional coefficient and at least one negative coefficient with solutions $x = 0$ and $x = \frac{4}{3}$.

Review

1. The Franklin Lee Middle School Glee Club is hosting a talent show competition to raise money for a community that was recently hit by a flood. All of the members are asked to go out in the community to sell tickets to the show.

   • Patrick sold 30 more tickets than Jose.

   • Gabriella sold 25 fewer than two times the number that Patrick sold.

   • Owen sold one-third the number of tickets that Patrick sold.

   • Desmond sold 15 fewer than Owen.

   a. Define a variable for the number of tickets Jose sold. Then write expressions for the number of tickets sold by the other students.

   b. If Jose sold 30 tickets, how many tickets did each of the others sell?

   c. If Gabriella sold 65 tickets, how many tickets did each of the others sell?

   d. If Patrick, Owen, and Desmond sold 175 tickets altogether, how many tickets did each of them sell?

2. Isabel surveyed three classes about their favorite season. The data from the survey are shown in the two-way table.

Student's Season Preference

		Winter	Spring	Summer	Fall	Total
Classes	**Class A**	9	2	7	6	24
	Class B	2	5	9	4	20
	Class C	8	6	10	4	28
	Total	19	13	26	14	72

(Column group header: Seasons)

a. Compute the relative frequencies for each row. If necessary, round decimals to the nearest thousandth.

b. What percent of students in Class A prefer winter?

c. Which class has the largest percent of students who prefer summer?

d. Compute the relative frequencies for each column. If necessary, round decimals to the nearest thousandth.

e. What percent of students who prefer winter are from Class C?

f. The smallest percentage of students who prefer summer comes from which class?

3. Determine whether each relation represents a function. Explain your reasoning.

a.

x	y
1	7
5	23
5	35
8	55

b.

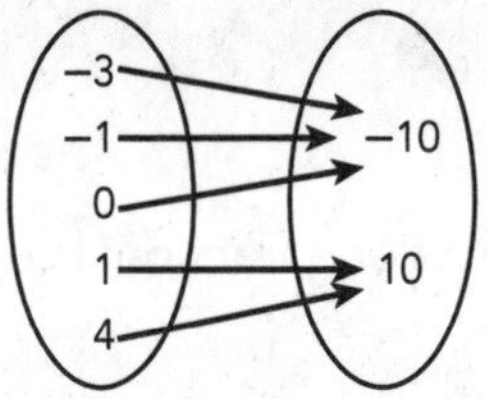

Solving Linear Equations Summary

Strategic Solving

An equation with variables on both sides of the equation can be solved by moving all the variable terms to one side of the equation and all the constants to the other side of the equation.

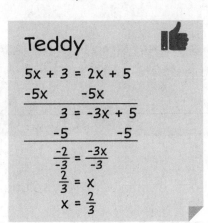

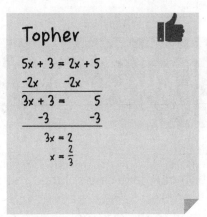

You can use Properties of Equality to rewrite equations and increase your efficiency with solving equations.

• Factor out a number from both sides.

Consider the equation $3x + 9 = 6x - 30$.
You can factor out the common factor 3 from both sides of the equation to help you solve.

$$\frac{3x + 9}{3} = \frac{6x - 30}{3} \quad \longrightarrow \quad x + 3 = 2x - 10 \quad \longrightarrow \quad 13 = x$$

- Multiply both sides of an equation by the least common denominator of the fractions to remove the fractions.

   Consider the equation $\frac{1}{3}(2x + 7) + \frac{5}{6} = \frac{5}{3}x$.

   You can multiply both sides of the equation by the least common denominator of the fractions to convert the fractions to whole numbers.

$\frac{1}{3}(2x + 7) + \frac{5}{6} = \frac{5}{3}x$	The LCD of the fractions is 6. Multiply both sides by 6.
$2(2x + 7) + 5 = 10x$	Rewrite using the Distributive Property.

- Multiply both sides of an equation by a power of 10 to remove decimals.

   Consider the equation $1.2x + 4.8 = 0.6x - 1.8$.

$10(1.2x + 4.8) = 10(0.6x - 1.8)$	$\longrightarrow$	Multiply both sides of the equation by 10.
$12x + 48 = 6x - 18$	$\longrightarrow$	Factor out a 6 from both sides.
$2x + 8 = x - 3$		

LESSON 2

MP3s and DVDs

A linear equation can have one solution, no solutions, or infinitely many solutions.

When the solution to the equation is a true statement with one value equal to the variable, there is only one solution. For example, the equation $x + 2 = 8$ has only one solution: $x = 6$.

When the solution to the equation is a false statement, the equation has no solution. For example, the equation $x + 0 = x + 1$ has no solutions.

When the solution to the equation is a true statement for any value of the variable, such as $x = x$, the equation has infinitely many solutions.

Equations can have different kinds of solutions.

For example, the equation $2x - 5 = 10$ has a positive rational solution: $x = \frac{15}{2}$.
The equation $2x + 5 = 0$ has a negative rational solution: $x = -\frac{5}{2}$.

Systems of Linear Equations

Intersections are important when solving systems of linear equations.

Module 3: Modeling Linear Equations

TOPIC 2: SYSTEMS OF LINEAR EQUATIONS

In this topic, students analyze and solve pairs of simultaneous linear equations. Throughout the topic, students write systems of equations to represent problem situations. To build fluency with solving systems of linear equations using inspection, graphing, and substitution, students write and solve additional systems of linear equations, using the structure of the equations in the system to determine the most efficient solution strategy.

Where have we been?

In this topic, students utilize a great deal of what they have learned in this course and previous courses about linear relationships, tables, graphs, and equations, and proportionality to solve problems and investigate solutions to multiple linear equations.

Where are we going?

Students' experiences in this topic provide the foundation for a more rigorous and abstract study of systems of equations in high school. In high school, students will solve systems that include equations that are not linear, and they will use algebraic and graphical techniques to solve systems of inequalities.

Modeling a Solution to a System with a Point of Intersection

If a system of two linear equations has one solution, that solution can be modeled as the point of intersection of the graphs of the two equations. For this system, when $x = 1$ and $y = 6$, both equations are true.

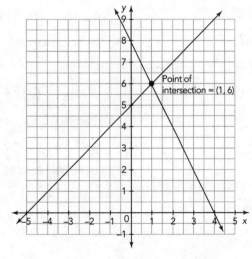

$$\begin{cases} y = x + 5 \\ y = -2x + 8 \end{cases}$$

Point of intersection = (1, 6)

Myth: Memory is like an audio or video recording.

Let's play a game. Memorize the following list of words: strawberry, grape, watermelon, banana, orange, peach, cherry, blueberry, raspberry. Got it? Good. Some believe that the brain stores memories in pristine form. Memories last for a long time and do not change—like a recording. Without looking back at the original list, was apple on it?

If you answered "yes," then go back and look at the list. You'll see that apple does not appear, even though it seems like it should. In other words, memory is an active, reconstructive process that takes additional information, like the category of words (e.g., fruit), and makes assumptions about the stored information.

This simple demonstration suggests memory is not like a recording. Instead, it is influenced by prior knowledge and decays over time. Therefore, students need to see and engage with the same information multiple times to minimize forgetting (and distortions).

#mathmythbusted

Talking Points

You can further support your student's learning by asking questions about the work they do in class or at home. Your student is learning more about systems of equations and solving systems.

Questions to Ask

- How does this problem look like something you did in class?
- Can you show me the strategy you used to solve this problem? Do you know another way to solve it?
- Does your answer make sense? How do you know?
- Is there anything you don't understand? How can you use today's lesson to help?

Key Terms

break-even point
When one graphed line represents the cost of an item and the other line represents the income from selling the item, the point of intersection is called the break-even point.

solution of a linear system
The solution of a linear system is an ordered pair (x, y) that is a solution to both equations in the system.

substitution method
The substitution method is a process of solving a system of equations by substituting a variable in one equation with an equivalent expression.

Crossing Paths

1

Point of Intersection of Linear Graphs

WARM UP

Determine an ordered pair (x, y) that represents a solution to each equation.

1. $y = 2x + 5$
2. $3x + 4y = 200$
3. $y = \frac{1}{2}x - 10$

LEARNING GOALS

- Write a system of equations to represent a problem situation.
- Analyze and solve a system of simultaneous linear equations graphically.
- Interpret the solution to a system of two linear equations in two variables as the point of intersection of two linear graphs and in terms of the original problem's context.
- Determine a point of intersection in a system of linear equations using tables.

KEY TERMS

- point of intersection
- break-even point

You have modeled different linear equations. How can you model two linear equations on the same graph? What does it mean when two linear graphs intersect?

Long-Sleeved T-Shirts

Profit is the amount of money made after paying all costs. To calculate the profit made from selling T-shirts, subtract the cost of the shirts from the income, which is the money earned from sales.

Your school's parent-teacher organization wants to sell long-sleeved T-shirts as a fundraiser. The business manager found a company that will charge $4 for each long-sleeved T-shirt and a setup fee of $160 to create the design that will be placed on each shirt. The chairman of the fundraising committee suggested selling the long-sleeved T-shirts for $8 each. The organization has asked you to help them analyze the production costs and the amount of money that can be made by this fundraiser.

1. If the shirts are sold for $8 each, at what point will the parent-teacher organization start making a profit? Show your work. Describe the reasoning you used to determine the answer.

Graphing and Interpreting a Point of Intersection

Consider the fundraiser being held by the parent-teacher organization, described in the previous activity. Shirts are sold for $8 each and cost $4 each to make, plus a $160 setup fee.

1. Write an equation to represent the organization's cost, in dollars, to buy the long-sleeved T-shirts. Describe what your variables represent.

2. Write an equation to represent the organization's income from selling the long-sleeved T-shirts. Describe what your variables represent.

3. Complete the table to show the cost, income, and profit for different numbers of long-sleeved T-shirts sold.

Quantity Name	Number of Long-Sleeved T-shirts	Cost	Income	Profit
Unit	Long-Sleeved T-shirts	Dollars	Dollars	Dollars
Expression				
	0			
	10			
	20			
	35			
	50			
	100			

4. Create graphs to represent the cost and the income on the coordinate plane shown. Use the given bounds and intervals.

Variable Quantity	Lower Bound	Upper Bound	Interval
Number of Long-Sleeved T-shirts	0	50	2.5
Money	0	400	20

Be sure to label your lines.

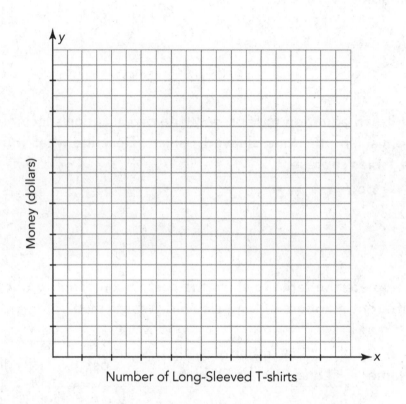

Money (dollars)

Number of Long-Sleeved T-shirts

5. Use your graphs to answer each question and describe your reasoning in terms of the graphs.

    a. Determine the number of long-sleeved T-shirts for which the cost is greater than the income.

    b. Determine the number of long-sleeved T-shirts for which the income is greater than the cost.

    c. Determine when the cost is equal to the income.

    d. Verify your solution algebraically.

The **point of intersection** is the point at which two lines cross on a coordinate plane. When one line represents the cost of an item and the other line represents the income from selling the item, the point of intersection is called the **break-even point**.

6. What is the break-even point for making and selling the long-sleeved T-shirts?

7. What is the profit from T-shirts at the break-even point?

8. What are the cost and income at the break-even point?

9. What do the coordinates of the point of intersection mean in terms of the fundraiser?

10. State the number of long-sleeved T-shirts that must be sold for a profit to be made.

A Different Point of Intersection

After the initial analysis, the business manager of the parent-teacher organization called the company that will be producing the shirts. The company agreed to discount the design fee to $80, while maintaining the cost of $4 per shirt. The committee would like you to analyze the profit potential with the new costs and a new selling price of $12 per shirt.

1. **Write an equation that represents the cost, in dollars, for the long-sleeved T-shirts. Describe what your variables represent.**

2. **Write an equation that represents the organization's income from selling the long-sleeved T-shirts. Describe what your variables represent.**

3. **Complete the table to show the cost, income, and profit for different numbers of long-sleeved T-shirts.**

Quantity Name	Number of Long-Sleeved T-shirts	Cost	Income	Profit
Unit	Long-sleeved T-shirts	Dollars	Dollars	Dollars
Expression				
	0			
	5			
	10			
	35			
	50			
	100			

4. **Create graphs to represent the cost and the income on the coordinate plane shown. Use the given bounds and intervals.**

Variable Quantity	Lower Bound	Upper Bound	Interval
Number of Long-Sleeved T-shirts	0	50	2.5
Money	0	400	20

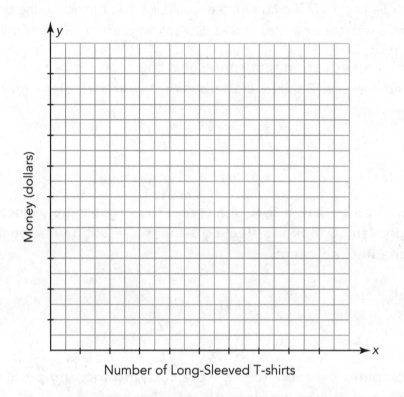

Number of Long-Sleeved T-shirts

5. **Use your graphs to answer each question and describe your reasoning in terms of the graphs.**

a. **Determine the number of long-sleeved T-shirts for which the cost is greater than the income.**

b. **Determine the number of long-sleeved T-shirts for which the income is greater than the cost.**

c. Determine when the cost is equal to the income.

d. Verify your solution algebraically.

6. What is the break-even point for producing and selling the long-sleeved T-shirts?

7. What is the profit from T-shirts at the break-even point?

8. What are the production cost and income at the break-even point?

9. What do the coordinates of the point of intersection mean in terms of the fundraiser?

10. State the number of long-sleeved T-shirts that must be sold for a profit to be made.

Serena is ordering lunch from Tony's Pizza Parlor. John told her that when he ordered from Tony's last week, he paid $34 for two 16-inch pizzas and two drinks. Jodi told Serena that when she ordered one 16-inch pizza and three drinks, it cost $23.

1. Write two equations to represent the two statements that Serena hears.

2. Interpret what the point of intersection means for the two lines representing the equations.

3. Verify your answers by graphing the two equations.

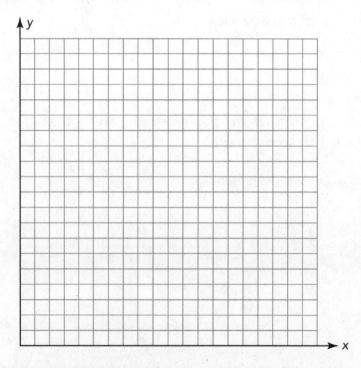

TALK the TALK

Putting It All on the Table

Look back at the tables you used in this lesson.

1. How can you use a table alone to determine the point of intersection of two linear graphs?

2. How does determining a point of intersection from a table compare with determining the point of intersection from a graph and from equations?

Assignment

Write

In your own words, define the terms *point of intersection* and *break-even point*.

Remember

The point where two linear graphs intersect represents the solution to both of the equations that describe the graphs.

Practice

Misha is the manager of Movie Parlor, a video store. She is in charge of buying the videos for the store to sell. She buys videos from a wholesaler that sells them for $8 each. The wholesaler also charges a fee of $200 for each bulk purchase. Misha then sells the videos for $12 each.

1. Write an equation to represent the cost to buy videos from the wholesaler. Describe what your variables represent. Write a second equation to represent the amount of money the store will earn from selling the videos. Describe what your variables represent in this equation.
2. Calculate the cost to buy 30 videos from the wholesaler.
3. Calculate the amount of money the store will earn from selling 30 videos.
4. Calculate the profit the store will make from selling 30 videos. Interpret the meaning of your answer.
5. Calculate the cost to buy 70 videos from the wholesaler.
6. Calculate the amount of money the store will earn from selling 70 videos.
7. Calculate the profit the store will make from selling 70 videos. Interpret the meaning of your answer.
8. Complete the table to show the cost of buying videos from the wholesaler and income for different numbers of videos.

Number of Videos	Cost from Wholesaler ($)	Income ($)
x		
0		
10		
30		
45		
70		
100		

9. Create graphs of both the cost and income equations. Use the given bounds and intervals.

Variable Quantity	Lower Bound	Upper Bound	Interval
Videos	0	70	5
Money	0	900	50

10. Use your graphs to determine the number of videos for which the cost to buy them is greater than the income from selling them. Explain your reasoning.

11. Use your graphs to determine the number of videos for which the income from selling them is greater than the cost to buy them. Explain your reasoning.

12. Determine the break-even point for buying and selling the videos.

13. What is the video store's profit at the break-even point?

14. What is the point of intersection of the two lines you graphed?

15. What do the coordinates of the point of intersection mean in terms of buying and selling videos?

16. Describe the number of videos that must be sold in order for a profit to be made.

Stretch

Suppose a jet plane is traveling at 500 miles per hour at a height of 30,000 feet. If you took off from the ground in a flying car, traveling straight up at 100 miles per hour, how far away would the plane need to be when you take off in order for the car to meet the plane at the same height and time?

Review

Determine whether the equation has one solution, no solutions, or infinite solutions.

1. $3x - 4 = 6x - 8$

2. $2x + 1 = 2x - 1$

Solve each equation.

3. $-4x - 2 = 6x + 2$

4. $\frac{1}{2}x - 5 = 8 + 2x$

Describe the pattern of association between the two quantities in each scatter plot.

5.

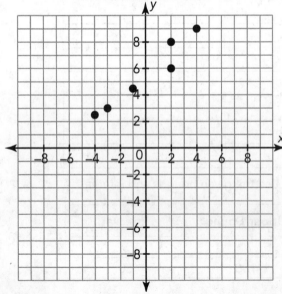

6.

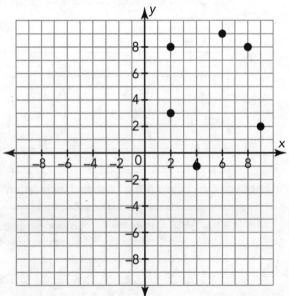

The Road Less Traveled

2

Systems of Linear Equations

WARM UP

1. Graph the equations on the coordinate plane.

   $y = x$

   $y = -x$

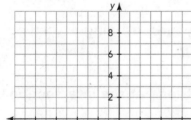

2. What are the coordinates of the point of intersection?

3. Interpret the meaning of the point of intersection.

LEARNING GOALS

- Write a system of equations to represent a problem context.
- Analyze and solve a system of two simultaneous linear equations in two variables graphically.
- Interpret the solution to a system of equations in terms of a problem situation.
- Use slope and y-intercept to determine whether two linear equations have one solution, no solutions, or infinite solutions.

KEY TERMS

- system of linear equations
- solution of a linear system
- consistent system
- inconsistent system

You have graphed linear equations on a coordinate plane. How can you interpret two linear equations together as a system?

According to the Map

Many of the diagonal roads in Washington, DC, are named after US states. Except for California and Ohio, every state provides the name for an avenue. California is a street, and Ohio is a drive. There is also a Puerto Rico Avenue.

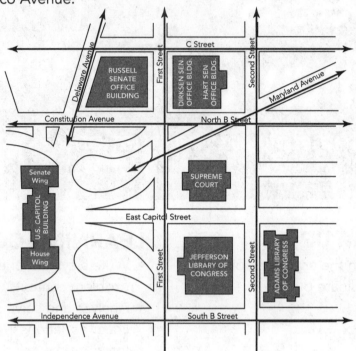

1. Answer each question and explain your reasoning according to the map shown.

    a. Would it be possible to meet a friend at the intersection of First Street and Second Street?

    b. Would it be possible to meet a friend at the intersection of Delaware Avenue and Constitution Avenue?

    c. Would it be possible to meet a friend at the intersection of C Street and Second Street?

2. How many places could you be if you are at the intersection of Independence Avenue and South B Street?

Representing a Problem Situation with a System of Equations

Colleen and Jimmy have part-time jobs after school. Both have decided that they want to see how much money they can save in one semester by placing part of their earnings each week into a savings account. Colleen currently has $120 in her account and plans to save $18 each week. Jimmy currently has $64 in his savings account and plans to save $25 each week.

1. Write an equation for Colleen and for Jimmy that represents the total amount of money, in dollars, in each of their savings accounts, *y*, in terms of the number of weeks, *x*, that they place money in their respective accounts.

2. How much money will each person have in his or her savings account after five weeks?

3. Which person will have more money in his or her savings account after five weeks?

4. How much money will each person have in his or her savings account after 18 weeks (the amount of time in one semester)?

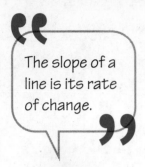

The slope of a line is its rate of change.

5. Which person will have more money in his or her savings account at the end of the semester?

6. Create a graph of each equation on the coordinate plane shown. Choose your bounds and intervals for each quantity.

Variable Quantity	Lower Bound	Upper Bound	Interval

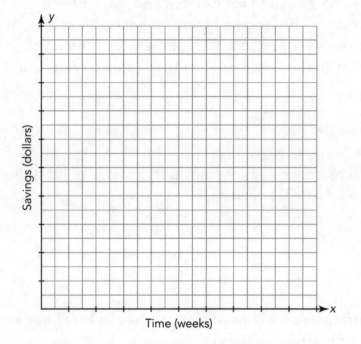

7. Determine the number of weeks after which Colleen and Jimmy will have the same amount of money in their savings accounts.

8. Verify your solution to Question 7 algebraically.

9. Interpret the meaning of the slope of each graph in this problem situation.

10. Which person is saving more money per week?

11. How can you tell who is saving more money each week by analyzing the graph?

12. Interpret the meaning of the *y*-intercept of each graph in this problem situation.

When two or more linear equations define a relationship between quantities, they form a **system of linear equations**. The **solution of a linear system** is an ordered pair (*x*, *y*) that is a solution to both equations in the system. Graphically, the solution is the point of intersection, the point at which two or more lines cross.

WORKED EXAMPLE

A system of linear equations is written with a brace as shown:

$$\begin{cases} y = x + 5 \\ y = -2x + 8 \end{cases}$$

You can determine the solution to this system by graphing the equations. The point of intersection is the solution to the system.

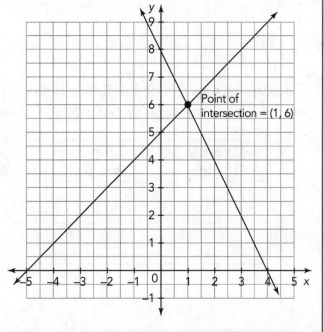

Point of intersection = (1, 6)

Systems with One Solution and No Solutions

Eric also has a part-time job after school working at the same place as Jimmy. He heard about the money that Colleen and Jimmy were saving and decided that he wanted to save money, also. Eric has $25 in his savings account and will save the same amount as Jimmy, $25 per week.

1. Write an equation that represents the total amount of money in Eric's savings account, y, in terms of the number of weeks, x, that he places money in his savings account.

2. Write a linear system that shows the total amount of money that will be saved by Eric and Jimmy.

3. Create a graph of the linear system on the coordinate plane shown. Choose your bounds and intervals for each quantity.

Variable Quantity	Lower Bound	Upper Bound	Interval

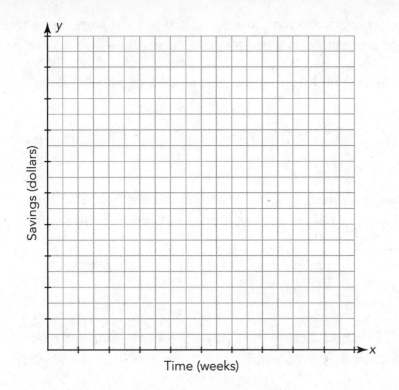

Time (weeks)

4. What does the slope of each graph represent in this problem situation?

5. What is the same for both Eric and Jimmy?

6. What is different for Eric and Jimmy?

7. What is the point of intersection for this system of equations? Explain your reasoning in terms of the graph.

The lines you graphed in Question 3 are parallel lines. Remember that two lines are parallel if they lie in the same plane and do not intersect.

8. What do you know about the slopes of parallel lines?

9. Does the linear system of equations for Eric and Jimmy have a solution? Explain your reasoning in terms of the graph.

10. Will Eric and Jimmy ever have the same amount of money in their savings accounts?

Eric's sister Trish was able to save $475 working part-time during the first semester of school. She recently quit her part-time job to play on the high school's softball team. She is hoping to get a college scholarship to play softball and wants to devote her time to achieving her goal. She will withdraw $25 each week from her savings account for spending money while she is not working.

11. Write an equation that gives the total amount of money in Trish's savings account, *y*, in terms of the number of weeks, *x*, that she withdraws money out of her savings account.

12. Write a system of equations that represents the amount of money that Trish and Eric will have in their respective savings accounts.

13. **Create a graph of the linear system on the coordinate plane shown. Choose your bounds and intervals for each quantity.**

Variable Quantity	Lower Bound	Upper Bound	Interval

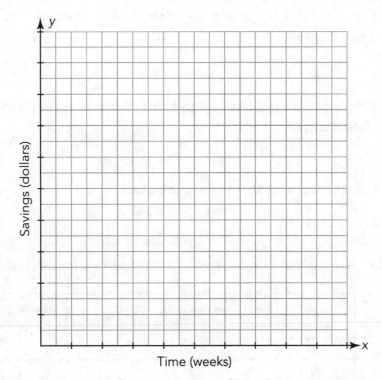

14. **What does the point of intersection of the lines represent?**

15. **Compare the slopes of the lines.**

16. **According to the graph, approximately when will Trish and Eric have the same amount of money in their savings accounts? How much will they each have?**

Systems with Infinitely Many Solutions

You have worked with systems of linear equations that have one solution and no solutions.

1. Describe the graphs in a system of linear equations that has one solution.

2. Describe the graphs in a system of linear equations that has no solution.

3. Consider the system of equations:

$$\begin{cases} y = 3x + 6 \\ y = 3(x + 2) \end{cases}$$

a. Complete the table of values for this linear system.

x	$y = 3x + 6$	$y = 3(x + 2)$
−2		
0		
2		
4		
8		
13		
20		

b. Describe the equations that make up this system. What can you conclude about the number of solutions to this type of linear equation?

TALK the TALK

Line Up for Inspection!

Each graph shows a system of two linear relationships.

1. Write the linear system that represents each.

a.

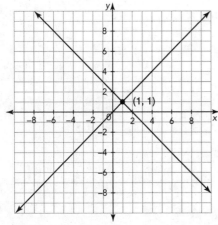

b.

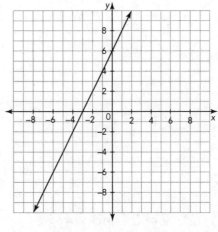

c.

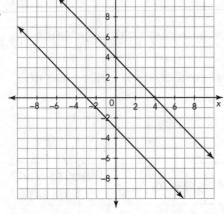

2. Using only the equations, determine whether each system has one solution, no solutions, or infinite solutions. Explain your reasoning.

   a. $y = \frac{4}{5}x - 3$ and $y = -\frac{5}{4}x + 6$

   b. $y = \frac{2}{3}x + 7$ and $y = \frac{1}{6}(4x + 42)$

   c. $y = -2.5x + 12$ and $y = 6 - 2.5x$

   d. $y = 5x$ and $y = \frac{1}{5}x$

A system of equations may have one unique solution, infinite solutions, or no solutions. Systems that have one or infinite solutions are called **consistent systems**. Systems that have no solution are called **inconsistent systems**.

3. Complete the table.

	Consistent Systems		Inconsistent Systems
	One Unique Solution	**Infinite Solutions**	**No Solutions**
Compare the slopes.			
Compare the y-intercepts.			
Describe the lines.			

Assignment

Write

Complete each sentence by writing the correct term or phrase from the lesson.

1. A(n) _____ is formed when the equations or graphs of two or more linear equations define a relationship between quantities.
2. A(n) _____ is an ordered pair (x, y) that is the point of intersection, the point at which two or more lines cross.
3. A(n) _____ has one or infinite solutions.
4. A(n) _____ has no solution.

Remember

- A system of equations whose graphs intersect at just one point is a system with one solution.
- A system of equations that has parallel line graphs is a system with no solutions.
- A system of equations that has identical graphs is a system with infinite solutions.

Practice

Aiko works in the fish department of a pet store. She is asked to drain, clean, and refill two reef tanks. The first tank holds 175 gallons of water, and the second tank holds 200 gallons of water. The hoses that she uses drain the tanks at a rate of 25 gallons of water per hour.

1. Write an equation for each tank that represents the total amount of water in gallons in the tank, y, in terms of the number of hours, x, that the tanks are draining.
2. How much water is in each tank after 3 hours?
3. Write your equations in the first row of the table. Then, complete the table of values for the linear system.

Number of Hours	First Tank	Second Tank
x		
0		
1		
2		
3		
4		
5		
6		
7		

4. Create a graph of both equations.
5. Interpret the meaning of the slope of each line in this problem situation.
6. What is the same for both tanks?
7. What is different for the two tanks?
8. What is the point of intersection for this system of equations? Explain your reasoning in terms of the graph.
9. When will both tanks have the same amount of water?
10. While Aiko is draining both tanks, she is also filling a 250-gallon tank. The water fills at a rate of 25 gallons per hour. Write an equation that gives the total amount of water in gallons in the third tank, y, in terms of the number of hours, x, that the tank is filling.

Stretch

A system with an equation that has an exponent of 2 can have more than one solution. How many solutions does the system $y = x$ and $y = x^2 - 2$ have? What are the solutions?

Review

1. Billy is selling lemonade for $1 per cup. It costs him 50 cents per cup to make the lemonade. He also has to spend an additional $10 for supplies such as ice, cups, and plastic shakers.
   a. Write a system of equations to represent this situation.
   b. What does the point of intersection represent in this situation?

2. Determine whether the equations have one solution, no solutions, or infinite solutions.
   a. $1.5x + 6.5 = \frac{3}{2}x + \frac{13}{2}$
   b. $-\frac{1}{5}x - 12 = -0.2x - \frac{24}{2}$

3. Solve each equation.
   a. $4(x + 5) = 6(x + 4)$
   b. $-3(p - 4) = -2p + 1$

The County Fair

3

Using Substitution to Solve Linear Systems

WARM UP

Analyze each system of equations. What can you conclude about the value of y in each?

1. $\begin{cases} x = 12 \\ y = x + 22 \end{cases}$

2. $\begin{cases} x = 0 \\ y = x - 45 \end{cases}$

3. $\begin{cases} x = y \\ y = 2x - 10 \end{cases}$

4. $\begin{cases} x = y + 3 \\ y = 2x - 10 \end{cases}$

LEARNING GOALS

- Write a system of equations to represent a problem context.
- Solve a system of equations algebraically using substitution.
- Interpret a solution to a system of linear equations in terms of the problem situation.
- Solve real-world and mathematical problems with two linear equations in two variables.

KEY TERMS

- standard form of a linear equation
- substitution method

Suppose you graph a system of equations, but the point of intersection is not clear from the graph? How can you determine the solution to the system?

Goats, Chickens, and Pigs

At the county fair, farmers bring some of their animals to trade with other farmers. To make all trades fair, a master of trade oversees all trades. Assume all chickens are of equal value, all goats are of equal value, and all pigs are of equal value.

- In the first trade of the day, 4 goats were traded for 5 chickens.
- In the second trade, 1 pig was traded for 2 chickens and 1 goat.
- In the third trade, Farmer Lyndi put up 3 chickens and 1 pig against Farmer Simpson's 4 goats.

1. Is this a fair trade? If not, whose animals are worth more? How could this be made into a fair trade?

Introduction to Substitution

In this lesson, you will explore systems of equations that may or may not be accurately solved using graphs. As you have seen, reasoning can also be used to solve systems. In the next activities, you will learn about solving systems algebraically.

Janet was helping her mother make potato salad for the county fair and was asked to go to the market to buy fresh potatoes and onions. Sweet onions cost $1.25 per pound, and potatoes cost $1.05 per pound. Her mother told her to use the $30 she gave her to buy these two items.

1. **Write an equation in standard form that relates the number of pounds of potatoes and the number of pounds of onions that Janet can buy for $30. Use *x* to represent the number of pounds of onions, and *y* to represent the number of pounds of potatoes that Janet can buy.**

2. **Janet's mother told her that the number of pounds of potatoes should be 8 times greater than the number of pounds of onions in the salad. Write an equation in *x* and *y* that represents this situation.**

3. **Will 1 pound of onions and 8 pounds of potatoes satisfy both equations? Explain your reasoning.**

The **standard form of a linear equation** is $Ax + By = C$, where A, B, and C are constants and A and B are not both zero.

4. Create graphs of both equations. Choose your bounds and intervals for each quantity.

Variable Quantity	Lower Bound	Upper Bound	Interval

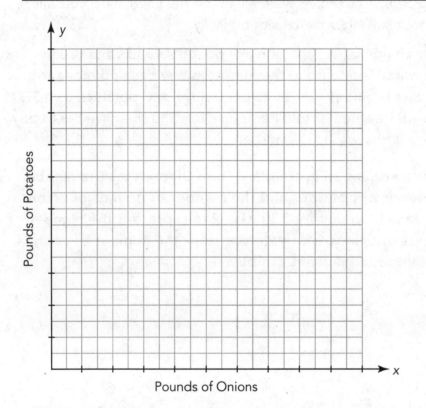

5. Can you determine the exact solution of this linear system from your graph? Explain your reasoning.

6. Estimate the point of intersection from your graph.

In many systems, it is difficult to determine the solution from the graph. There is an algebraic method that can be used called the *substitution method*. The **substitution method** is a process of solving a system of equations by substituting a variable in one equation with an equivalent expression.

WORKED EXAMPLE

Let's consider the system you wrote.

$$\begin{cases} 1.25x + 1.05y = 30 \\ y = 8x \end{cases}$$

Because $y = 8x$ is in slope-intercept form, use this as the first equation.

Step 1: To use the substitution method, begin by choosing one equation and isolating one variable. This will be considered the first equation.

Step 2: Now, substitute the expression equal to the isolated variable into the second equation.

Substitute $8x$ for y in the equation $1.25x + 1.05y = 30$.

Write the new equation.

$$1.25x + 1.05y = 30$$
$$1.25x + 1.05(8x) = 30$$

You have just created a new equation with only one unknown.

Step 3: Solve the new equation.

$$1.25x + 8.40x = 30$$
$$9.65x = 30$$
$$x \approx 3.1$$

Therefore, Janet should buy approximately 3.1 pounds of onions.

Now, substitute the value for x into $y = 8x$ to determine the value of y.

$$y = 8(3.1) = 24.8$$

Therefore, Janet should buy approximately 24.8 pounds of potatoes.

Step 4: Check your solution by substituting the values for both variables into the original system to show that they make both equations true.

Keep in mind what the value represents.

7. Check that the solution is correct. Show your work.

8. What is the solution to the system? What does it represent in terms of the problem situation?

9. Compare your solution using the substitution method to the solution on your graph. What do you notice?

Substitution with Special Systems

Samson and Adrian are helping to set up the booths at the fair. They are each paid $7 per hour to carry the wood that is needed to build the various booths. Samson arrives at 7:00 A.M. and begins working immediately. Adrian arrives 90 minutes later and starts working.

1. Write an equation that gives the amount of money that Samson will earn, y, in terms of the number of hours he works, x.

2. How much money will Samson earn after 90 minutes of work?

3. Write an equation that gives the amount of money Adrian will earn, y, in terms of the number of hours since Samson started working, x.

4. How much money will each student earn by noon?

5. Will Adrian ever earn as much money as Samson? Explain your reasoning.

6. Write a system of linear equations for this problem situation.

7. Analyze the system of linear equations. What do you know about the solution of the system by observing the equations? Explain your reasoning.

> How is this similar to solving linear equations with no solution or with infinite solutions?

Let's see what happens when we solve the system algebraically.

8. Since both equations are written in slope-intercept form as expressions for y in terms of x, substitute the expression from the first equation into the second equation.

   a. Write the new equation.

   b. Solve the equation for x.

   c. Does your result for x make sense? Explain your reasoning.

9. What is the result when you algebraically solve a linear system that contains parallel lines?

On Monday night, the fair is running a special for the the local schools: if tickets are purchased from the school, you can buy student tickets for $4 and adult tickets for $4. You buy 5 tickets and spend $20.

10. Write an equation that relates the number of student tickets, x, and the number of adult tickets, y, to the total amount spent.

11. Write an equation that relates the number of student tickets, x, and the number of adult tickets, y, to the total number of tickets purchased.

12. Write both equations in slope-intercept form.

13. Analyze the system of linear equations. What do you know about the solution of the system by looking at the equations?

Let's see what happens when you solve the system algebraically.

14. Since both equations are now written in slope-intercept form as expressions for y in terms of x, substitute the expression from the first equation into the second equation.

   a. Write the new equation and solve the equation for x.

   b. Does your result for x make sense? Explain your reasoning.

15. How many student tickets and adult tickets did you purchase?

16. What is the result when you algebraically solve a linear system that contains two lines that are actually the same line?

Solving Systems by Substitution

Write and solve a system of equations to solve each problem.

1. The admission fee for the fair includes parking, amusement rides, and admission to all commercial, agricultural, and judging exhibits. The cost for general admission is $7, and the price for children under the age of 5 is $4. There were 449 people who attended the fair on Thursday. The admission fees collected amounted to $2768.

   a. Write a system of equations in standard form for this situation. Use x to represent the number of people 5 and over, and use y to represent the number of children under 5 years of age.

   b. Without solving the system of linear equations, interpret the solution.

   c. Solve the system of equations using the substitution method. Then interpret the solution of the system in terms of the problem situation.

2. The business manager for a band must make $236,000 from ticket sales to cover costs and make a reasonable profit. The auditorium where the band will play has 4000 seats, with 2800 seats on the main level and 1200 on the upper level. Attendees will pay $20 more for main-level seats.

   a. Write a system of equations with x representing the cost of the main-level seating and y representing the cost of the upper-level seating.

   b. Without solving the system of linear equations, interpret the solution.

   c. Solve the system of equations using the substitution method. Then interpret the solution of the system in terms of the problem situation.

3. Ms. Ross told her class that tomorrow's math test will have 20 questions and be worth 100 points. The multiple-choice questions will be 3 points each, and the open-ended response questions will be 8 points each. Determine how many multiple-choice and open-ended response questions will be on the test.

a. Write a system of equations. Describe your variables.

b. Without solving the system of linear equations, interpret the solution.

c. Solve the system of equations using the substitution method. Then interpret the solution of the system in terms of the problem situation.

4. Ashley is working as a cashier at the sports arena. What should she tell the next person in line?

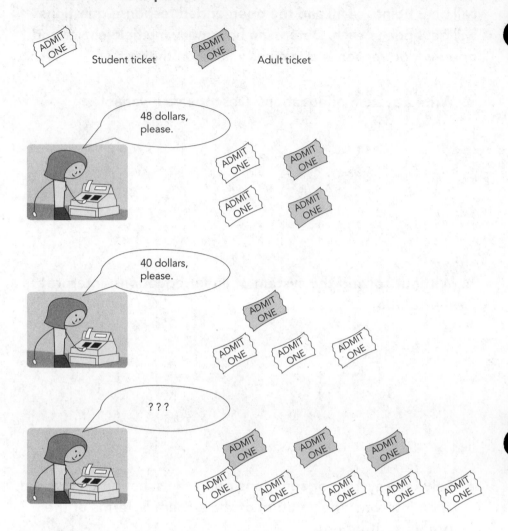

Write and solve a system of equations that represents the problem situation. Define the variables. Then determine the cost of each type of ticket. Finally, state the amount Ashley charges the third person.

5. Alex is applying for positions at two different electronic stores in neighboring towns. The first job offer is a $200 weekly salary plus 5% commission on sales. The second job offer is a $75 weekly salary plus 10% commission.

a. Write a system of equations that represents the problem situation. Define the variables. Then solve the system of linear equations and interpret the solution in terms of the problem situation.

b. What is the difference in the weekly pay between stores if Alex sells $3000?

c. What is the difference in the weekly pay if he sells $4225?

d. Which job offer would you recommend Alex take? Explain your reasoning.

Alex's sales targets for each job would be between $1500 and $3000 weekly. Each manager tells Alex the same thing: "Some weeks are better than others, depending on the time of year and the new releases of technology."

TALK the TALK

The Substitution Train

1. Determine the solution to each linear system by using the substitution method. Check your answers algebraically.

a. $\begin{cases} 2x + 3y = 34 \\ y = 5x \end{cases}$

b. $\begin{cases} y = 4x + 2 \\ y = 3x - 2 \end{cases}$

c. $\begin{cases} 3x + 2y = 4 \\ 2x - y = 5 \end{cases}$

d. $\begin{cases} 3x + y = 8 \\ 6x + 2y = 10 \end{cases}$

Assignment

Write

Explain how to use the substitution method to solve systems of linear equations.

Remember

When a system has no solution, the equation resulting from the substitution step has no solution.

When a system has infinite solutions, the equation resulting from the substitution step has infinite solutions.

Practice

1. Serena is trying to become more environmentally conscious by making her own cleaning products. She researches different cleaners and decides to make furniture polish using olive oil and lemon juice. She wants to make enough to fill two 24-ounce bottles.

   a. Write an equation in standard form that relates the amount of olive oil and lemon juice to the total amount of mixture Serena wants to make. Use x to represent the amount of lemon juice and y to represent the amount of olive oil.

   b. The recommendation for the mixture is that the amount of olive oil be twice the amount of lemon juice. Write an equation in terms of x and y as defined in part (a) that represents this situation.

   c. Use substitution to solve the system of equations. Check your answer.

   d. What does the solution of the system represent in terms of the mixture?

   e. The best price Serena can find for lemon juice is $0.25 per ounce. The best price she can find for olive oil is $0.39 per ounce. She buys a total of 84 ounces of lemon juice and olive oil, and spends $29.40. Write equations in standard form for this situation. Use x to represent the amount of lemon juice she buys, and use y to represent the amount of olive oil she buys.

   f. Solve the system of equations you wrote using the substitution method. Check your answer. Describe the solution in terms of the problem situation.

2. In an effort to eat healthier, Bridget is tracking her food intake by using an application on her phone. She records what she eats, and then the application indicates how many calories she has consumed.
   One day, Bridget eats 10 medium strawberries and 8 vanilla wafer cookies as an after-school snack. The caloric intake from these items is 192 calories. The next day, she eats 20 medium strawberries and 1 vanilla wafer cookie as an after-school snack. The caloric intake from these items is 99 calories.

   a. Write a system of equations for this problem situation. Define your variables.

   b. Without solving the system of linear equations, interpret the solution.

   c. Solve the system of equations using the substitution method. Check your work.

   d. Interpret the solution of the system in terms of the problem situation.

   e. Bridget's friend Monica also has a calorie counting application on her phone. The two friends decide to compare the two programs. Bridget eats 1 banana and 5 pretzel rods, and her application tells her she consumed 657 calories. Monica eats 1 banana and 5 pretzel rods, and her application tells her she consumed 656 calories. The girls want to know how many calories are in each food. Write a system of equations for this problem. Define your variables.

   f. Solve the system of equations using the substitution method. Interpret your answer in terms of the problem.

3. Write a system of linear equations to represent each situation. Then solve the system using substitution. Interpret the solution of the system in terms of the problem situation.

    a. James has 13 coins. The coins are nickels and quarters. The coins have a total value of $2.05. Let n represent the number of nickels, and let q represent the number of quarters.

    b. Ms. Snyder is giving a 28-question test that is made up of 2-point questions and 4-point questions. The entire test is worth 100 points. Let t represent the number of 2-point questions, and let f represent the number of 4-point questions.

    c. The basketball team scored 82 points from 2-point and 3-point baskets. They make 38 baskets altogether. Let a represent the number of 2-point baskets, and let b represent the number of 3-point baskets.

4. Use the substitution method to determine the solution of each system of linear equations. Check your solutions.

    a. $\begin{cases} 9x + y = 16 \\ y = 7x \end{cases}$
        b. $\begin{cases} 3x + \frac{1}{2}y = -3.5 \\ y = -6x + 11 \end{cases}$

    c. $\begin{cases} y = -5x \\ 21x - 7y = 28 \end{cases}$
        d. $\begin{cases} 2x + 4y = -32 \\ y = -\frac{1}{2}x - 8 \end{cases}$

Stretch

Create a system of linear equations with solution (2, 5). Solve the system using substitution to verify your system has the given solution.

Review

1. Graph each system of linear equations to determine the solution to the system.

    a. $y = 34 - \frac{5}{2}x$ and $y = \frac{2}{5}x + 5$ b. $y = 21x + 144$ and $y = 3(7x + 48)$

2. The population growth (in thousands) for a small town near Bay City can be represented by the expression $x + \frac{4}{5}(x + 315)$, where x represents the number of years since 2005. The population growth (in thousands) for a neighboring town can be represented by the expression $2x - \frac{1}{5}(x - 630)$, where x represents the number of years since 2005. When will the populations of the two towns be the same?

3. Two neighboring towns are not having population growth. In fact, they both have been losing population since 1995. The population decline for one of the towns (in thousands) can be represented by the expression $-\frac{2}{5}(x - 500)$, where x represents the number of years since 1995. The population decline for the other town (in thousands) can be represented by the expression $-\frac{1}{2}x + \frac{1}{10}(x + 2000)$, where x represents the number of years since 1995. When will the populations of the two towns be the same?

4. Solve each equation.

    a. $8(2m + 7) = 10(m + 11)$ b. $-3(y + 20) = -9y$

Rockin' Roller Rinks

4

Choosing a Method to Solve a Linear System

WARM UP

By inspection, determine if each system has no solution, infinite solutions, or one solution.

1. $\begin{cases} y = 4x - 14 \\ y = -4x - 14 \end{cases}$

2. $\begin{cases} y = 4x - 14 \\ y - 4x = -14 \end{cases}$

3. $\begin{cases} y = 4x - 14 \\ y = 4x + 14 \end{cases}$

4. $\begin{cases} y = 4x - 14 \\ 4x - y = 14 \end{cases}$

LEARNING GOALS

- Write a system of linear equations to represent a problem context.
- Interpret the solution of a system of linear equations.
- Choose the best method to solve a system of linear equations.

Now that you know how to solve systems of linear equations by graphing, by inspection, and by substitution, how do you decide which method to use?

So Many Possibilities

Tickets for a movie cost $8 for evenings and $5 for matinees. There were 440 tickets sold, and $3130 was collected in ticket sales.

1. Consider each system of equations. Determine which system(s) could be used to calculate the number of matinee tickets sold. Explain your reasoning.

   a. $\begin{cases} x + y = 3130 \\ 5x + 8y = 440 \end{cases}$

   b. $\begin{cases} x + y = 440 \\ 5x + 8y = 3130 \end{cases}$

   c. $\begin{cases} x + y = 3130 \\ 8x + 5y = 440 \end{cases}$

   d. $\begin{cases} x + y = 440 \\ 8x + 5y = 3130 \end{cases}$

2. Consider the valid system(s) from Question 1. How would you solve each valid system: by graphing or by substitution? Explain your reasoning.

Comparing Two Fee Schedules

The activities director of the Community Center is planning a skating event for all the students at the local middle school. There are several skating rinks in the area, but the director does not know which one to use. At a previous event at Skate Park the director initially paid $230 for a party of 10, but when 20 students attended she ended up paying $260. For a different event at Roller Rama, she paid $125 for 25 students, but ended up paying $200 when 40 students attended.

Assume that the skating rinks have not changed their rates for skating parties.

1. Define variables to represent the total cost and the number of students attending the event.

2. Write and interpret an equation for the total cost of using Skate Park in terms of the number of students attending.

3. Write and interpret an equation for the total cost of using Roller Rama in terms of the number of students attending.

4. Suppose the activities director anticipates that 50 students will attend.

   a. Calculate the total cost of using Skate Park.

   b. Calculate the total cost of using Roller Rama.

5. Suppose the activities director has $650 to spend on the skating event.

   a. Determine the number of students who can attend if the event is held at Skate Park.

   b. Determine the number of students who can attend if the event is held at Roller Rama.

6. Write a system of equations to represent this problem situation.

7. **Solve this system using each strategy. Interpret the meaning of the solution in the context of the problem situation.**

You can use a variety of strategies and representations to solve a system of linear equations.

- inspection
- table
- graph
- substitution

Table

Number of Students	Skate Park	Roller Rama

Graph

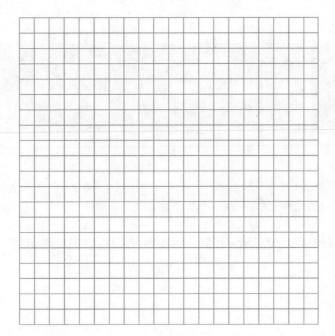

Substitution

8. Which skating rink would you recommend to the activities director? Explain your reasoning.

9. Explain the advantages and disadvantages of using each strategy.

table   graph   substitution

ACTIVITY
4.2

A Third Equation

Super Skates offers the use of the rink for a flat fee of $1000 for an unlimited number of skaters.

1. Write a linear equation to represent this situation.

"Can you determine the point of intersection on the graph?"

2. Add a column to the table in the previous activity for Super Skates. Also, graph the equation for Super Skates on the grid in the previous activity.

3. Use substitution to determine when Super Skates is the same price as Skate Park and Roller Rama. In which case did you need to use substitution to determine the solution?

4. Describe when going to Super Skates is a better option than going to Skate Park or Roller Rama. Explain your reasoning.

5. Explain under what conditions you would recommend each skating rink to the director of the Community Center based solely on the cost to rent each skating rink.

> Look at the structure of each system before you choose your solution strategy.

Solve each linear system. State what elements of each system led to your chosen solution strategy.

1. $\begin{cases} y = 5x + 12 \\ y = 9x - 4 \end{cases}$

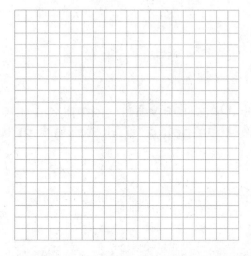

2. $\begin{cases} 8x + 3y = 30 \\ 8x + 3y = 16 \end{cases}$

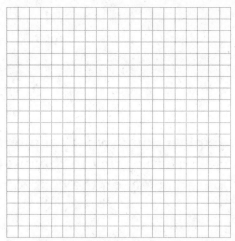

3. $\begin{cases} 4y = 11 - 3x \\ 3x + 2y = -5 \end{cases}$

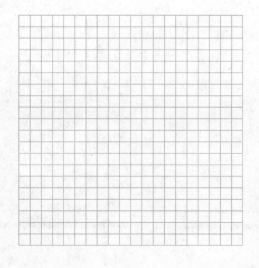

4. $\begin{cases} 15x + 28y = 420 \\ 30x + 24y = 720 \end{cases}$

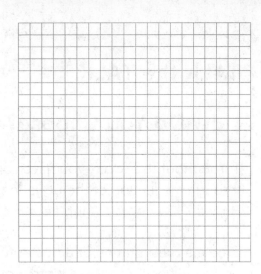

5. $\begin{cases} 3x + 2y = 6 \\ 1.5x + y = 3 \end{cases}$

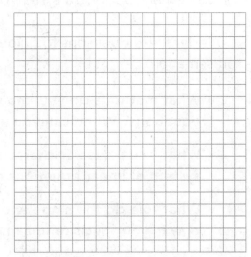

6. $\begin{cases} 4x + 3y = 27 \\ \frac{1}{3}x = 2y + 1 \end{cases}$

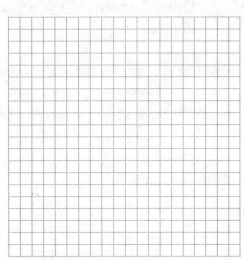

TALK the TALK 💬

How Do You Choose?

Throughout this topic, you have solved systems of linear equations through inspection of the equations, graphing, and substitution. How do you decide when each method is most efficient?

Create a presentation or a poster to illustrate your decision-making process when you solve a system of linear equations.

Consider these questions to guide the content of your presentation.

- **What methods do you know for solving systems of linear equations? When can you use each one?**

- **What visual cues or characteristics of the equations in the system of linear equations guide your decision?**

- **What role do the slope and *y*-intercept of the equations play in your decision-making?**

- **Does the form of the equations in the system affect your choice?**

Use the systems of linear equations you solved throughout this lesson to support your reasoning and as examples of when you would choose each solution method.

List at least three key points that you want to include in your presentation.

1.

2.

3.

Assignment

Write

Explain why you may need to use substitution to solve a system of linear equations if you already solved the system by graphing.

Remember

To most efficiently solve a system of linear equations, look at the equations in the system. The coefficients and constants in the equations can help you choose the best solution method.

Practice

1. Rent-A-Wreck rents cars for $50 a day, plus $0.25 per mile. Drive-A-Lemon rents cars for $40 a day, plus $0.30 per mile.

   a. Write a system of equations that best models the cost of renting a car from each business. Let x represent the number of miles, and let y represent the cost per day.

   b. Solve the system using your chosen method.

   c. Interpret the solution of the linear system in terms of the problem situation.

   d. In what situations would you recommend renting a car from Rent-A-Wreck?

2. Rika works in the perfume department at Hoover's Department Store. She is giving away samples of a new fragrance and a new scented hand lotion to customers that pass by her station. She is required to hand out a total of 114 samples during her shift. She has already handed out 36 samples, which represents $\frac{1}{3}$ of the number of fragrance samples and $\frac{1}{4}$ of the number of hand lotion samples that she must hand out.

   a. Write a system of equations for this problem situation. Let x represent the number of fragrance samples, and let y represent the number of hand lotion samples.

   b. Solve the system using your chosen method.

   c. Interpret the solution of the linear system in terms of the problem situation.

3. Belinda works in the kitchen department of Hoover's Department Store. As part of the store's effort to reward their customers, Belinda is handing out coupons for two different types of silverware packages. The first coupon is for the classic set, and the second coupon is for the modern set. On one particular day, she has handed out a total of 144 coupons, which represents $\frac{1}{2}$ of the number of classic coupons and $\frac{3}{4}$ of the number of modern coupons. She handed out twice as many coupons for the modern set as she did for the classic set.

   a. Write a system of equations for this problem situation. Let x represent the number of coupons for the classic set, and let y represent the number of coupons for the modern set.

   b. Solve the system using your chosen method.

   c. Interpret the solution of the linear system in terms of the problem situation.

4. Ms. Jupino is the leader of her daughter's Girl Scout troop, which has 15 members. The troop would like to take an end-of-year field trip to an amusement park, but they need to raise money for the trip. They have researched different fundraising companies and have narrowed their search down to two. Both companies have fundraising opportunities that involve selling coupon booklets. The first company, Great Ideas, will donate $50 if the troop uses their company, plus the girls will make $10 for every booklet that they sell. The second company, Paper and Things, will donate $275 if the troop uses their company, plus the girls will make $7 for every booklet that they sell.

   a. Write a system of equations that represents the problem situation. Define your variables.

   b. Solve the system using your chosen method.

   c. Interpret the solution of the linear system in terms of the problem situation.

   d. Which company would you recommend the girls use? Explain.

5. Solve each system using your chosen method.

   a. $\begin{cases} 3x - 2y = 9 \\ -3x + y = -12 \end{cases}$
        b. $\begin{cases} 5x - 3y = 30 \\ \frac{5}{3}x - 10 = y \end{cases}$

   c. $\begin{cases} 2x + 6y = 12 \\ x + 3y = 4 \end{cases}$
        d. $\begin{cases} 2x + 2y = 4 \\ 2y = x - 17 \end{cases}$

Stretch

You can also use inequalities to solve problems that involve systems. Suppose the Community Center director who was planning the skating party has a budget of $895.

Write and solve an inequality to determine the number of students who can be invited to each of the three locations. Then interpret each solution in terms of the problem situation.

Review

1. Write and solve each system using substitution.

   a. You want to make your grandmother's recipe for fudge. You have all the ingredients except sugar and chocolate. You have $10.50 to spend on the sugar and chocolate. Sugar costs $1.40 per pound, and chocolate costs $8.40 per pound. Your grandmother's recipe calls for 4 times as much sugar as chocolate. How much sugar and chocolate can you buy?

   b. Your piggy bank contains 68 coins, made up of quarters and dimes. The piggy bank gives a digital readout of the total amount of money that it contains. The display reads $13.10. How many quarters and dimes do you have?

2. Solve each equation.

   a. $4(2x + 1) - 3(x - 2) = 10 + 5x$
        b. $10(x - 2) + 15 = 8x + 7$

   c. $2(x + 3) + 2 = 2(x + 4)$
        d. $3(2x + 2) = 6(x + 6)$

Systems of Linear Equations Summary

KEY TERMS

- point of intersection
- break-even point
- system of linear equations
- solution of a linear system

- consistent system
- inconsistent system
- standard form of a linear equation
- substitution method

LESSON 1 | Crossing Paths

The **point of intersection** is the point at which two lines cross on a coordinate plane. When one line represents the cost of an item and the other line represents the income from selling the item, the point of intersection is called the **break-even point**.

The point where two linear graphs intersect represents the solution to both of the equations that describe the graphs.

For example, Jenna plans to sell hats that she knits at the local craft fair. The cost for a booth at the fair is $100 and each hat costs her $5 to make. She plans to sell each hat for $25. Jenna's total cost for selling the hats can be represented by the equation $y = 100 + 5x$, while her income can be represented by the equation $y = 25x$. The graph of each equation is shown. The point of intersection is (5, 125). This point represents the break-even point because it will cost Jenna $125 to make 5 hats, and her income from selling 5 hats is $125.

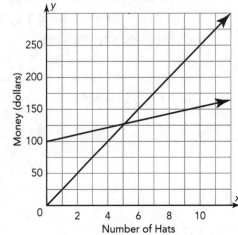

The Road Less Traveled

When two or more linear equations define a relationship between quantities, they form a **system of linear equations**. The **solution of a linear system** is an ordered pair (x, y) that is a solution to both equations in the system. Graphically, the solution is the point of intersection, the point at which two or more lines cross.

A system of linear equations is written with a brace as shown:

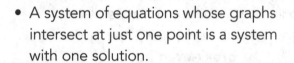

$$\begin{cases} y = x + 5 \\ y = -2x + 8 \end{cases}$$

You can determine the solution to this system by graphing the equations. The point of intersection is the solution to the system.

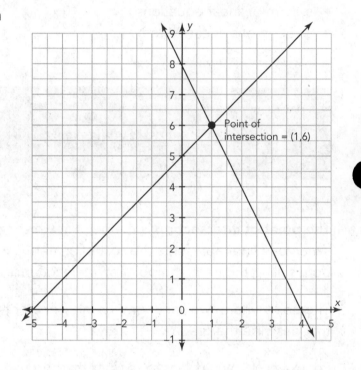

Point of intersection = (1,6)

- A system of equations whose graphs intersect at just one point is a system with one solution.

- A system of equations that has parallel line graphs is a system with no solutions. These equations will have equal slopes, but different *y*-intercepts.

- A system of equations that has identical graphs is a system with infinitely many solutions.

The **standard form of a linear equation** can be written as $ax + by = c$, where a, b, and c are constants, and a and b are not both zero.

Sometimes a system of equations may not be accurately solved using graphs. There is an algebraic method that can be used called the substitution method. The **substitution method** is a process of solving a system of equations by substituting a variable in one equation with an equivalent expression.

For example, consider the system of equations.

$$\begin{cases} 1.25x + 1.05y = 30 \\ y = 8x \end{cases}$$

Step 1: To use the substitution method, begin by choosing one equation and isolating the variable. This will be considered the first equation. Because $y = 8x$ is in slope-intercept form, use this as the first equation.

Step 2: Now, substitute the expression equal to the isolated variable into the second equation. Substitute $8x$ for y in the equation $1.25x + 1.05y = 30$. Write the new equation: $1.25x + 1.05(8x) = 30$.

Step 3: Solve the new equation.

$$1.25x + 8.40x = 30$$
$$9.65x = 30$$
$$x \approx 3.1$$

Now, substitute the value for x into $y = 8x$ to determine the value for y.

$$y \approx 8(3.1) \approx 24.8$$

Step 4: Check your solution by substituting the values for both variables into the original system to show that they make both equations true.

When a system has no solution, the equation resulting from the substitution step has no solution. When a system has infinite solutions, the equation resulting from the substitution step has infinite solutions.

To most efficiently solve a system of linear equations, look at the equations in the system. The coefficients and constants in the equations can help you choose the best solution method—either through inspection of the equations, graphing, or substitution.

For example, both of the equations in this system are written in standard form, so you may choose to solve the system of equations using substitution:

$$\begin{cases} x + y = 440 \\ 5x + 8y = 3130 \end{cases}$$

However, suppose you are solving this other system of equations.

$$\begin{cases} y = 2x + 2 \\ y = x - 1 \end{cases}$$

Because both of the equations are written in slope-intercept form, you may choose to solve this system of equation using graphing.

MODULE 4

EXPANDING NUMBER SYSTEMS

The lessons in this module connect number, equations, and geometry. You will explore the properties that define the number systems that you are familiar with and then learn about a new system. You will develop an understanding of the Pythagorean Theorem and its converse and then apply those theorems to solve real-world problems.

The Real Number System

Pi is probably one of the most famous numbers in all of history. As a decimal, it goes on and on forever without repeating.

Module 4: Expanding Number Systems

TOPIC 1: THE REAL NUMBER SYSTEM

In this topic, students build onto their knowledge of number systems to include the set of irrational numbers. Students will review writing fractions as decimals and then write repeating decimals in fractional form. They learn that numbers that are not rational are called irrational; the decimal form of irrational numbers does not terminate or repeat. Students also use square root and cube root symbols to express the solutions to equations of the form $x^2 = p$ and $x^3 = p$, where p is a positive rational number.

Where have we been?

The first lesson of this topic provides students the opportunity to recall number sets they should already know before learning about properties of each set and about irrational numbers. Students also review additive identity, additive inverse, multiplicative identity, and multiplicative inverse.

Where are we going?

This topic prepares students to solve problems with non-perfect squares in the next topic, *Pythagorean Theorem*. Students need to understand that mathematics is not arbitrary; every new number system they learn results from a need for a number that is not in the current known number systems. Studying identities, inverses, and closure helps students understand that each number system has unique properties.

Using Perfect Squares to Estimate Square Roots

The square root of a number can be estimated using the square roots of perfect squares. For example, $\sqrt{10}$ is between $\sqrt{9}$, which is 3, and $\sqrt{16}$, which is 4. So, $3 < \sqrt{10} < 4$.

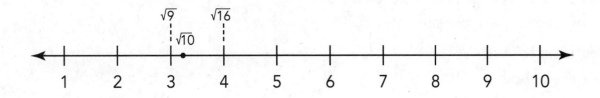

Myth: Cramming for an exam is just as good as spaced practice for long-term retention.

Everyone has been there. You have a big test tomorrow, but you've been so busy that you haven't had time to study. So you had to learn it all in one night. You may have gotten a decent grade on the test. However, did you to remember the material a week, month, or year later?

The honest answer is, "probably not." That's because long-term memory is designed to retain useful information. How does your brain know if a memory is "useful" or not? One way is the frequency in which you encounter a piece of information. If you only see something once (like during cramming), then your brain doesn't deem those memories as important. However, if you sporadically come across the same information over time, then it's probably important. To optimize retention, encourage your student to periodically study the same information over expanding intervals of time.

#mathmythbusted

Talking Points

You can further support your student's learning by resisting the urge, as long as possible, to get to the answer in a problem that your student is working on. Students are encountering irrational numbers formally for the first time in this topic. They will need time and space to struggle with all the implications of working with this expanded number system. Practice asking good questions when your student is stuck.

Questions to Ask

- Let's think about this. What are all the things you know?
- What do you need to find out?
- How can you model this problem?

Key Terms

irrational numbers
Decimals that represent irrational numbers cannot be written as fractions in the form $\frac{a}{b}$, where a and b are integers and b is not equal to 0.

real numbers
Combining the set of rational numbers and the set of irrational numbers produces the set of real numbers.

So Many Numbers, So Little Time

Number Sort

WARM UP

Represent each number as a fraction, decimal, and percent.

1. $\frac{5}{8}$
2. 105%
3. 0.55

LEARNING GOALS

- Review and analyze numbers.
- Determine similarities and differences among various numbers.
- Sort numbers by their similarities and rationalize the differences between groups of numbers.

You have been using numbers to count and perform calculations for nearly your entire life. If someone were to ask you to define the word *number*, could you do it? How can you identify and organize different types of numbers?

Gimme, Gimme, Gimme!

1. List three numbers that are positive numbers.

2. List three numbers that are between 0 and 1.

3. Give one example of a percent.

4. Give one example of a fraction.

5. Give one example of a mixed number.

A Number Sort

Searching for patterns and sorting objects into different groups can provide valuable insights.

1. Cut out the 30 number cards located at the end of the lesson. Then, analyze and sort the numbers into different groups. You may group the numbers in any way you feel is appropriate. However, you must sort the numbers into more than one group.

   In the space provided, record the information for each of your groups.

   - Name each group of numbers.
   - List the numbers in each group.
   - Provide a rationale for why you created each group.

> Are any of the types of numbers shared among your groups? Or are they unique to each group?

2. Compare your groupings with your classmates' groupings. Create a list of the different types of numbers you noticed.

Taking a Closer Look at the Number Sort

Did you use any rationale similar to these students?

In this activity, you will analyze the ways in which other students grouped the numbers and their rationale.

1. Lauren grouped these numbers together.

$$0.\overline{91}, \ -\frac{2}{3}, \ \frac{100}{11}, \ 1.523232323\ldots, \ -0.\overline{3}$$

Why do you think Lauren put these numbers in the same group?

2. Zane and Tanya provided the same rationale for one of their groups of numbers. However, the numbers in their groups were different.

Zane

$|-3|, \ \sqrt{100}, \ 627{,}513, \ 3.21 \times 10^{12}, \ 4^2, \ |2|$

When I simplify each number, it is a positive integer.

Tanya

$20\%, \ \sqrt{100}, \ 627{,}513, \ 3.21 \times 10^{12}, \ 4^2, \ |2|, \ 212\%$

Each of these numbers represents a positive integer.

Who is correct? Explain your reasoning.

3. Tim grouped these numbers together.

$-\frac{3}{8}$, -101, -6.41, $-\frac{2}{3}$, $-\sqrt{9}$, -1, $-0.\overline{3}$

What rationale could Tim provide?

4. Isaac grouped all the numbers between 0 and 1.

Identify all of the numbers that satisfy Isaac's reasoning.

Clip all your numbers together and keep them. You'll need them later in this topic.

5. Lezlee grouped these numbers together.

-6.41, $\frac{100}{11}$, $1.523232323...$, 212%, $6\frac{1}{4}$

What could Lezlee name the group? Explain your reasoning.

TALK the TALK

Match 'Em Up

Match each group of numbers with the appropriate group name. Explain your reasoning for each.

1. 1.5, $\frac{5}{3}$, -212.2, 16.12, $-\frac{6}{5}$ A. Negative Numbers

2. $-\frac{6}{3}$, -200, -0.5, $-50.313...$, -1 B. Integers

3. -0.75, 20%, 3.5%, -0.005, $\frac{1}{5}$, $-\frac{1}{2}$ C. Improper Fractions

4. -10, 50, 2100, 10^2, 5^3, 400%, 0 D. Numbers Between -1 and 1

π	0.25	$-\dfrac{3}{8}$
-101	20%	$\lvert -3 \rvert$
-6.41	$0.\overline{91}$	$\sqrt{100}$
627,513	0.001	$-\dfrac{2}{3}$
0	$\sqrt{2}$	3.21×10^{12}
1,000,872.0245	4^2	0.5%
$-\sqrt{9}$	$\lvert 2 \rvert$	$\dfrac{100}{11}$
$-\sqrt{2}$	$1.523232323\ldots$	-1
$-0.\overline{3}$	1.0205×10^{-23}	$\sqrt{\dfrac{9}{16}}$
212%	$6\dfrac{1}{4}$	$\sqrt{0.25}$

Assignment

Write

Describe the characteristics that you look for in numbers when you are grouping them.

Remember

Numbers can be grouped in a variety of ways according to their characteristics. Sometimes, a number may fit into multiple groupings.

Practice

Ling's teacher gives her students the list of numbers to sort.

$$5\%, \ -3^3, \ \sqrt{0.36}, \ 2.14, \ |-6|, \ \tfrac{12}{18}, \ 15, \ \overline{4}, -\tfrac{16}{3}, \ \pi, \ \sqrt{\tfrac{4}{10}}, \ 8003.876, \ 0.2\%, \ -\sqrt{25}, \ 3\tfrac{1}{3}$$

1. Ling groups the following numbers together with the rationale that they are all repeating decimals.

$$\tfrac{12}{18}, \ -\tfrac{16}{3}, \ 3\tfrac{1}{3}$$

   Do you agree with Ling's grouping? Explain your reasoning.

2. Ling groups the following numbers together with the rationale that they are all positive numbers.

$$5\%, \ \sqrt{0.36}, \ 2.14, \ |-6|, \ \tfrac{12}{18}, \ 15, \ \sqrt{4}, \ \pi, \ \sqrt{\tfrac{4}{10}}, \ 8003.876, \ 0.2\%, \ 3\tfrac{1}{3}$$

   Do you agree with Ling's grouping? Explain your reasoning.

3. Ling groups the following numbers together with the rationale they are all rational numbers.

$$\tfrac{12}{18}, \ 15, \ \sqrt{4}, \ -\tfrac{16}{3}, \ 3\tfrac{1}{3}$$

   Do you agree with Ling's grouping? Explain your reasoning.

Stretch

What is so interesting about the fraction $\tfrac{16}{64}$? This fraction is called a *digit-canceling fraction*, since you can cross out the common digit in the numerator and denominator and the value of the fraction remains the same.

$$\frac{1\cancel{6}}{\cancel{6}4} = \frac{1}{4}$$

There are exactly four digit-canceling fractions with two-digit numerators and two-digit denominators that are less than one, not counting examples such as $\tfrac{30}{50}$, where you cross out the zeros. Research these special fractions and identify the other three.

Review

1. A company makes and sells flags with various seasonal themes. It costs $12 to manufacture each flag, and there is a set-up cost of $200 for a new design. The company sells the flags to home improvement stores for $20 per flag.

   a. Write a system of equations to represent this situation.

   b. What is the break-even point for making and selling flags? Show your work.

2. The school dance team is raising money by charging admission to the spring ballet. They charge $2 for each student ticket and $5 for each adult ticket, with a goal to raise $510 from ticket sales.

   a. If they sell 50 student tickets, how many adult tickets do they need to sell to reach their goal?

   b. If they sell 30 adult tickets, how many student tickets to they need to sell to reach their goal?

3. Solve each equation.

   a. $3(n - 5) = 7 - 2(n + 1)$

   b. $2(5k + 8) = 4(k + 4)$

Rational Decisions

Rational and Irrational Numbers

2

WARM UP

1. Place $\frac{5}{8}$ and $\frac{6}{25}$ on the number line.

2. Rewrite $\frac{5}{8}$ as a decimal.

3. Rewrite $\frac{6}{25}$ as a decimal.

4. Place the decimal equivalents of $\frac{5}{8}$ and $\frac{6}{25}$ on the number line.

5. Are your strategies to plot fractions the same or different than your strategies to plot decimals?

LEARNING GOALS

- Determine under which operations (addition, subtraction, multiplication, and division) number sets are closed.
- Recognize that all numbers can be written as decimals and that rational numbers can be written as terminating or repeating decimals.
- Write repeating decimals as fractions.
- Identify numbers that are not rational as irrational numbers.

KEY TERMS

- natural numbers
- whole numbers
- integers
- closed
- rational numbers
- irrational numbers
- terminating decimal
- repeating decimal
- bar notation

You have learned about rational numbers. How are they different from other number sets?

A Science Experiment

A science class is conducting an experiment to see how the weight of a paper airplane affects the distance that it can fly. The class is divided into two groups. Group 1 measures the distance the airplane flew in feet. Group 2 measures the distance in meters, and then converts those measurements to feet. The results of the experiment are shown in the table.

Because paper is typically sold in 500-sheet quantities, a paper's weight is determined by the weight of 500 sheets of the paper.

Type of Paper	Group 1 Measurements	Group 2 Converted Measurements
20-pound paper	$13\frac{7}{8}$ feet	13.9 feet
28-pound paper	$14\frac{3}{8}$ feet	14.4 feet

1. The science class needs to compare the measurements between the two groups for each type of paper.

   a. Write $13\frac{7}{8}$ as a decimal.   b.   Write $14\frac{3}{8}$ as a decimal.

2. On the number line shown, graph the Group 1 measurements written as decimals and the Group 2 converted measurements.

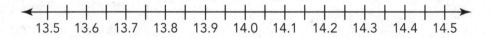

13.5   13.6   13.7   13.8   13.9   14.0   14.1   14.2   14.3   14.4   14.5

3. Use the number line to determine which group's paper airplane traveled farther for the 20-pound paper and for the 28-pound paper. Write your answers using complete sentences.

ACTIVITY 2.1 Natural Numbers, Whole Numbers, and Integers

The first set of numbers that you learned when you were very young was the set of *counting numbers*, or *natural numbers*. **Natural numbers** consists of the numbers that you use to count objects: {1, 2, 3, …}.

In the set {1, 2, 3, …}, the dots at the end of the list mean that the list of numbers goes on without end.

1. Consider the set of natural numbers.

   a. Why do you think this set of numbers is sometimes referred to as the set of counting numbers?

   b. How many natural numbers are there?

   c. Does it make sense to ask which natural number is the greatest? Explain why or why not.

You have also used the set of *whole numbers*. **Whole numbers** are made up of the set of natural numbers and the number 0, the additive identity.

2. Why is zero the additive identity?

3. Explain why having zero makes the set of whole numbers more useful than the set of natural numbers.

Use braces to represent sets.

Another set of numbers is the set of **integers**, which is a set that includes all of the whole numbers and their additive inverses.

4. **What is the additive inverse of a number?**

5. **Represent the set of integers. Use set notation and remember to use three dots to show that the numbers go on without end in both directions.**

6. **Does it make sense to ask which integer is the least or which integer is the greatest? Explain why or why not.**

When you perform an operation such as addition or multiplication on the numbers in a set, the operation could produce a defined value that is also in the set. When this happens, the set is said to be **closed** under the operation.

The set of integers is said to be closed under the operation of addition. This means that for every two integers a and b, the sum $a + b$ is also an integer.

7. **Determine if each set of numbers is closed under the given operation. Provide an example to support your response.**

   a. **Are the natural numbers closed under addition?**

   b. **Are the whole numbers closed under addition?**

c. Are the natural numbers closed under subtraction?

d. Are the whole numbers closed under subtraction?

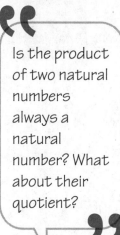

Is the product of two natural numbers always a natural number? What about their quotient?

e. Are the integers closed under subtraction?

f. Are any of these sets closed under multiplication?

g. Are any of these sets closed under division?

In previous courses, you have learned about the additive inverse, the multiplicative inverse, the additive identity, and the multiplicative identity.

8. Consider each set of numbers and determine if the set has an additive identity, additive inverse, multiplicative identity, or a multiplicative inverse. Explain your reasoning for each.

a. the set of natural numbers

A set of numbers must include an identity to also include the related inverse.

b. the set of whole numbers

c. the set of integers.

ACTIVITY 2.2 Rational Numbers

New number systems arise out of a need to create new types of numbers. If you divide two integers, what type of number have you created? You've created a *rational number*.

A **rational number** is a number that can be written in the form $\frac{a}{b}$, where a and b are both integers and b is not equal to 0.

1. Consider how each set of numbers is related. Answer each question and provide an example to support your response.

   a. Does the set of rational numbers include the set of whole numbers?

   b. Does the set of rational numbers include the set of integers?

   c. Does the set of rational numbers include all fractions?

   d. Does the set of rational numbers include all decimals?

2. Determine if the set of rational numbers is closed under the given operation. Provide an example to support your response.

a. addition

b. subtraction

c. multiplication

d. division

3. Determine whether the set of rational numbers contains the identity or inverse given. Provide an example to support your response.

a. additive identity

b. multiplicative identity

c. additive inverse

d. multiplicative inverse

You have seen some numbers such as π that are not rational numbers. There are other numbers that are not rational numbers. For example, $\sqrt{2}$ and $\sqrt{5}$, which are called square roots, cannot be written in the form $\frac{a}{b}$, where a and b are both integers.

As you will see in the next lesson, even though you often approximate square roots using a decimal, most square roots are *irrational numbers*. Because all rational numbers can be written as $\frac{a}{b}$, where a and b are integers, they can be written as *terminating decimals* (e.g., $\frac{1}{4} = 0.25$) or *repeating decimals* (e.g., $\frac{1}{6} = 0.1666...$).

All other decimals are **irrational numbers,** because these decimals cannot be written as fractions in the form $\frac{a}{b}$, where a and b are integers and b is not equal to 0.

Does "repeating decimal" mean that only one digit repeats?

1. **Convert the fraction to a decimal by dividing the numerator by the denominator. Continue to divide until you see a pattern. Describe the pattern.**

   $\frac{1}{3} = 3\overline{)1}$

2. Order the fractions from least to greatest. Then, convert each fraction to a decimal by dividing the numerator by the denominator. Continue to divide until you see a pattern.

a. $\frac{5}{6} = 6\overline{)5}$

b. $\frac{2}{9} = 9\overline{)2}$

c. $\frac{9}{11} = 11\overline{)9}$

d. $\frac{3}{22} = 22\overline{)3}$

3. Explain why these decimal representations are called repeating decimals.

A **terminating decimal** is a decimal that has a finite number of non-zero digits. For instance, the decimal 0.125 is a terminating decimal, because it has three non-zero digits. 0.125 is the decimal equivalent of $\frac{1}{8}$, because 1 divided by 8 is equal to 0.125.

A **repeating decimal** is a decimal with digits that repeat in sets of one or more. You can use two different notations to represent repeating decimals. One notation shows one set of digits that repeats with a bar over the repeating digits. This is called **bar notation**.

$$\frac{1}{3} = 0.\overline{3} \qquad\qquad \frac{7}{22} = 0.3\overline{18}$$

Another notation shows two sets of the digits that repeat with dots to indicate repetition. You saw these dots as well when describing the number sets in the previous lesson.

$$\frac{1}{3} = 0.33... \qquad\qquad \frac{7}{22} = 0.31818...$$

> Do you write $\frac{7}{22}$ as 0.318... or as 0.3181...?

4. **Write each repeating decimal from Question 2 using both notations.**

a. $\frac{5}{6}$

b. $\frac{2}{9}$

c. $\frac{9}{11}$

d. $\frac{3}{22}$

Some repeating decimals represent common fractions, such as $\frac{1}{3}$, $\frac{2}{3}$, and $\frac{1}{6}$, and are used often enough that you can recognize the fraction by its decimal representation. For most repeating decimals, though, you cannot recognize the fraction that the decimal represents. For example, can you tell which fraction is represented by the repeating decimal 0.44... or $0.\overline{09}$? In these cases, you need a method for converting from a repeating decimal to a fraction.

WORKED EXAMPLE

You can use algebra to determine the fraction that is represented by the repeating decimal 0.44… . First, write an equation by setting the decimal equal to a variable that will represent the fraction.

$$w = 0.44\ldots$$

Next, write another equation by multiplying both sides of the equation by a power of 10. The exponent on the power of 10 is equal to the number of decimal places until the decimal begins to repeat. In this case, the decimal begins repeating after 1 decimal place, so the exponent on the power of 10 is 1. Because $10^1 = 10$, multiply both sides by 10.

$$10w = 4.4\ldots$$

Then, subtract the equations.

$$
\begin{aligned}
10w &= 4.44\ldots \\
-w &= 0.44\ldots \\
\hline
9w &= 4
\end{aligned}
$$

Finally, solve the equation by dividing both sides by 9.

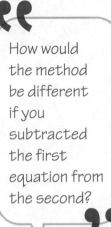

> How would the method be different if you subtracted the first equation from the second?

---

5. **Identify the fraction represented by the repeating decimal 0.44….**

6. **Use this method to write the fraction that represents each repeating decimal.**

   a. 0.55…   b. 0.0505…

   c. $0.\overline{12}$ d. $0.\overline{36}$

TALK the TALK

Closing Time

Complete the table to summarize the number sets you have learned about and reviewed in this lesson. Provide examples for each number set to address the four operations of addition, subtraction, multiplication, and division.

Number Set	Description	Closed under these operations. Provide examples.	Not closed under these operations. Provide examples.
Natural Numbers			
Whole Numbers			
Integers			
Rational Numbers			

Assignment

Write

Match each term with the number that best represents that term.

1. Irrational number
2. Terminating decimal
3. Repeating decimal
4. Bar notation

a. $\frac{1}{2} = 0.5$
b. $0.\overline{3}$
c. π
d. $\frac{5}{9} = 0.555...$

Remember

All rational numbers can be written as terminating or repeating decimals. A repeating decimal is a decimal in which one or more digits repeat indefinitely. A terminating decimal is a decimal that has a finite number of non-zero digits.

Practice

1. Marcy Green is the manager for her high school softball team. She is in charge of equipment, as well as recording statistics for each player on the team. The table shows some batting statistics for the four infielders on the team during the first eight games of the season.

Player	At Bats	Hits
Brynn Thomas	36	16
Hailey Smith	32	12
Serena Rodrigez	33	11
Kata Lee	35	14

a. In order to compare the batting averages of the players, Marcy must convert all of the ratios of hits to at-bats to decimal form. Determine the batting averagev for each player, and continue to divide until you see a pattern. Write your answers using both dots and bar notation for repeating decimals.

b. Write the batting averages of the players in order from lowest to highest. Who has the best batting average so far?

c. Marcy keeps track of how many home runs each infielder hits on the high school softball team. For each player, the fraction of home runs per at-bats is given in decimal form. Determine how many home runs each player has had so far.

   - Brynn: $0.0\overline{5}$
   - Hailey: 0.15625
   - Serena: $0.\overline{12}$
   - Kata: 0.2

2. Tell whether the numbers in each problem are natural numbers, whole numbers, integers, or rational numbers, and state whether those numbers are closed under the operation used.

   a. $-12 \div (-5)$

   b. $\frac{3}{7} + \left(-\frac{3}{8}\right)$

3. Convert each fraction to a decimal. State whether the fraction is equivalent to a terminating or repeating decimal.

   a. $1\frac{2}{5}$

   b. $\frac{5}{12}$

   c. $\frac{5}{8}$

   d. $\frac{8}{11}$

4. Write each repeating decimal as a fraction.

   a. $0.\overline{8}$

   b. 0.5454...

   c. 0.0777...

   d. $0.\overline{185}$

Stretch

Numbers can be operated on using operations other than addition, subtraction, multiplication, and division. Let's define a new operation called ✲, where $2 ✲ 4 = 2^2 \div 4$ and $6 ✲ 3 = 6^6 \div 3$. Is the set of whole numbers closed under the operation ✲? That is, does $a ✲ b$, where a and b are whole numbers, always result in a whole number? Justify your claim.

Review

1. Provide a rationale for each grouping of numbers.

   a. $3, \frac{75}{5}, -18, -\frac{30}{3}$

   b. 25%, $\frac{7}{11}$, 0.912912..., 0.5%

2. Write and solve a system of equations for each problem situation. Interpret the solution in terms of the context.

   a. Pedro has 97 athlete cards. In his collection, he has 39 more baseball player cards than football player cards. How many of each type of card does Pedro have?

   b. The Ryans are researching venues for their family reunion. The Picnic Place charges $150 to reserve a picnic shelter and $20 per hour to use the shelter. Totally Tents charges $300 for the rental and setup of a tent and $10 per hour to use their land. When would the cost be the same at both The Picnic Place and Totally Tents? What is that cost?

3. Solve each equation.

   a. $6(x + 3) = 3(2x + 5) - 3$

   b. $-5(x + 4) = 2(x - 10)$

What Are Those?!

The Real Numbers

3

Warm Up

Rewrite each fraction as a decimal.

1. $\frac{1}{2}$

2. $\frac{1}{4}$

3. $\frac{1}{3}$

4. $\frac{1}{9}$

5. How are the decimals of the first two fractions different from the decimals of the second two fractions?

LEARNING GOALS

- Identify irrational numbers.
- Identify the square roots of numbers that are not perfect squares and the cube roots of numbers that are not perfect cubes as irrational numbers.
- Use rational approximations of irrational numbers to compare the size of irrational numbers.
- Locate irrational numbers on a number line and estimate their values.
- Classify numbers within the set of real numbers.

KEY TERMS

- perfect cube
- cube root
- index
- real numbers
- Venn diagram

You have learned about rational numbers and about irrational numbers. In this lesson, you will learn about some special irrationals. Putting the set of rational numbers and the set of irrational numbers together forms the set of real numbers.

An Irrational Assignment?

1. Write an irrational number.

2. Have a classmate verify whether or not your number is an irrational number. Explain why your number is or is not an irrational number.

Recall that a square root is one of two equal factors of a given number. Every positive number has two square roots: a positive square root and a negative square root.

For instance, 5 is a square root of 25 because (5)(5) = 25. Also, −5 is a square root of 25 because (−5)(−5) = 25. The positive square root is called the principal square root. In this course, you will only use the principal square root.

The symbol $\sqrt{}$ is called a radical, and it is used to indicate square roots. The radicand is the quantity under a radical.

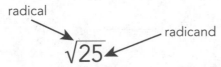

radical

radicand

$\sqrt{25}$

This is read as "the square root of 25," or as "radical 25."

Remember that a perfect square is a number that is equal to the product of a distinct factor multiplied by itself. In the example above, 25 is a perfect square because it is equal to the product of 5 multiplied by itself.

1. **Write the square root for each perfect square.**

    a. $\sqrt{1}$ = _____

    b. $\sqrt{4}$ = _____

    c. $\sqrt{9}$ = _____

    d. $\sqrt{16}$ = _____

    e. $\sqrt{25}$ = _____

    f. $\sqrt{36}$ = _____

    g. $\sqrt{49}$ = _____

    h. $\sqrt{64}$ = _____

    i. $\sqrt{81}$ = _____

    j. $\sqrt{100}$ = _____

    k. $\sqrt{121}$ = _____

    l. $\sqrt{144}$ _____

    m. $\sqrt{169}$ = _____

    n. $\sqrt{196}$ _____

    o. $\sqrt{225}$ _____

2. What is the value of $\sqrt{0}$? Explain your reasoning.

3. Notice that the square root of each expression in Question 1 resulted in a rational number. Do you think that the square root of every number will result in a rational number? Explain your reasoning.

4. Use a calculator to evaluate each square root. Show each answer to the hundred-thousandth.

a. $\sqrt{25}$ = _____   b. $\sqrt{0.25}$ = _____   c. $\sqrt{250}$ = _____

d. $\sqrt{5}$ = _____   e. $\sqrt{-25}$ = _____   f. $\sqrt{2.5}$ = _____

g. $\sqrt{2500}$ = _____   h. $\sqrt{676}$ = _____   i. $\sqrt{6760}$ = _____

j. $\sqrt{6.76}$ = _____   k. $\sqrt{67.6}$ = _____   l. $\sqrt{-6.76}$ = _____

5. What do you notice about the square roots of rational numbers? Justify your response.

6. Is the square root of a whole number always a rational number? Justify your response.

7. Is the square root of a decimal always an irrational number?

8. Consider Penelope and Martin's statements and reasoning.

Penelope
I know that 144 is a perfect square. Therefore, $\sqrt{144}$ is a rational number. I can move the decimal point to the left, and $\sqrt{14.4}$ and $\sqrt{1.44}$ will also be rational numbers.

Likewise, I can move the decimal point to the right, so $\sqrt{1440}$ and $\sqrt{14,400}$ will also be rational numbers.

Martin
I know that 144 is a perfect square. Therefore, $\sqrt{144}$ is a rational number. I can move the decimal point two places to the right or left to get another perfect square rational number. In other words, $\sqrt{1.44}$ and $\sqrt{14,400}$ will also be rational numbers.

Moving the decimal point two places at a time is like multiplying or dividing by 100. The square root of 100 is 10, which is also a rational number.

Who is correct? Explain your reasoning.

Estimating with Square Roots

The square root of most numbers is not an integer. You can *estimate* the square root of a number that is not a perfect square. Begin by determining the two perfect squares closest to the radicand so that one perfect square is less than the radicand, and one perfect square is greater than the radicand. Then consider the location of the expression on a number line and use approximation to estimate the value.

WORKED EXAMPLE

To estimate $\sqrt{10}$ to the nearest tenth, identify the closest perfect square less than 10 and the closest perfect square greater than 10.

The closest perfect square less than 10:	The square root you are estimating:	The closest perfect square greater than 10:
9	$\sqrt{10}$	16

You know:

$$\sqrt{9} = 3 \qquad\qquad\qquad\qquad \sqrt{16} = 4$$

This means that the estimate of $\sqrt{10}$ is between 3 and 4.

Locate each square root on a number line. The approximate location of $\sqrt{10}$ is closer to 3 than to 4 when plotted.

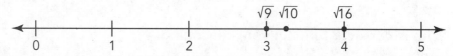

Think about the location of $\sqrt{10}$ in relation to the values of 3 and 4.

Therefore, $\sqrt{10} \approx 3.2$.

The symbol ≈ means approximately equal to.

1. **Calculate the square of 3.2 to determine if it is a good estimation of $\sqrt{10}$. Adjust the estimated value if necessary.**

2. Consider each expression.

$$\sqrt{8} \qquad \sqrt{91} \qquad \sqrt{70} \qquad \sqrt{45}$$

To locate the approximation of a square root on a number line, identify the two closest perfect squares, one greater than the radicand and one less than the radicand.

a. Order the expressions from least to greatest.

b. Locate the approximation of each expression on the number line. Explain the strategy you used to plot each value.

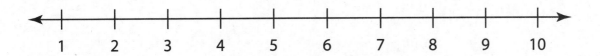

c. Estimate the value of each expression to the nearest tenth. Then, calculate the square of each approximation to determine if it is a good estimation. Adjust the estimated value, if necessary.

3. Solve each equation. Round your answer to the nearest tenth.

If $x^2 = 4$, then $x = \sqrt{4}$. Use this fact to show the solution to each equation.

a. $x^2 = 25$

b. $a^2 = 13$

c. $c^2 = 80$

d. $g^2 = 53$

In the previous activity, you investigated squares and square roots. Now, let's consider cubes and cube roots.

1. Use unit cubes to build three different cubes with the given side lengths. Then complete the table.

   a. 1 unit

   b. 2 units

   c. 3 units

Dimensions of Each Cube	Total Number of Unit Cubes
$4 \times 4 \times 4$	

The formula for the volume of a cube is $V = s \times s \times s$, which can be written as $V = s^3$.

You just calculated the volume of 3 cubes whose side lengths were the first 3 counting numbers, $1^3 = 1$, $2^3 = 8$, and $3^3 = 27$. The numbers 1, 8, and 27 are called *perfect cubes*. A perfect cube is the cube of a whole number. For example, 64 is a perfect cube since 4 is a whole number, and $4 \times 4 \times 4 = 64$. To calculate the cube of a number, you multiply the number by itself 3 times.

2. Calculate the cubes of the first 10 whole numbers.

$1^3 = $ _____ $2^3 = $ _____

$3^3 = $ _____ $4^3 = $ _____

$5^3 = $ _____ $6^3 = $ _____

$7^3 = $ _____ $8^3 = $ _____

$9^3 = $ _____ $10^3 = $ _____

If you know the volume of a cube, you can work backwards to calculate the side lengths of the cube. For example, to determine the side lengths of a cube that has a volume of 125, you need to determine what number used as a factor 3 times will equal 125. Since $5 \times 5 \times 5 = 125$, a side length of the cube is 5, and 5 is called the *cube root* of 125. A **cube root** is one of 3 equal factors of a number. As with the square root, the cube root also uses a radical symbol but has a 3 as an *index*: $\sqrt[3]{1}$. The **index** is the number placed above and to the left of the radical to indicate what root is being calculated.

The cube root of a number that is not a perfect cube is often an irrational number.

3. Write the cube root for each perfect cube.

$\sqrt[3]{1} = $ _____ $\sqrt[3]{8} = $ _____

$\sqrt[3]{27} = $ _____ $\sqrt[3]{64} = $ _____

$\sqrt[3]{125} = $ _____ $\sqrt[3]{216} = $ _____

$\sqrt[3]{343} = $ _____ $\sqrt[3]{512} = $ _____

$\sqrt[3]{729} = $ _____ $\sqrt[3]{1000} = $ _____

4. What is the side length of the largest cube you can create with 729 cubes?

5. Will the cube root of a number always be a whole number? If not, provide an **example** of a cube root that is not an integer.

Remember, the radicand is under the $\sqrt{}$.

Most numbers do not have whole numbers for their cube root. Let's estimate the cube root of a number using the same method used to estimate the square root of a number.

WORKED EXAMPLE

To estimate $\sqrt[3]{33}$ to the nearest tenth, first identify the two perfect cubes closest to the radicand. One of the perfect cubes must be less than the radicand, and the other must be greater than the radicand. Then consider the location of the expression on a number line and use approximation to estimate the value.

The closest perfect cube less than 33:	The cube root you are estimating:	The closest perfect cube greater than 33:
27	$\sqrt[3]{33}$	64

You know:
$\sqrt[3]{27} = 3$ $\sqrt[3]{64} = 4$

This means that the estimate of $\sqrt[3]{33}$ is between 3 and 4.

Locate the approximate value of $\sqrt[3]{33}$ on a number line

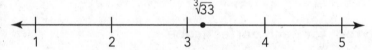

Next, choose decimals between 3 and 4, and calculate the cube of each decimal to determine which one is the best estimate.

Consider: $(3.2)(3.2)(3.2) = 32.768$
            $(3.3)(3.3)(3.3) = 35.937$

Therefore, $\sqrt[3]{33} \approx 3.2$.

6. Identify the two closest perfect cubes, one greater than the radicand and one less than the radicand. Then locate the approximation of each expression on a number line. Finally, estimate each cube root to the nearest tenth.

a. $\sqrt[3]{100}$

b. $\sqrt[3]{175}$

c. $\sqrt[3]{256}$

7. Solve each equation. Round to the nearest tenth.

a. $x^3 = 27$

b. $a^3 = 31$

c. $c^3 = 512$

-101 -6.41

$-\sqrt{9}$ $-\sqrt{2}$

-1 $-\frac{2}{3}$

$-\frac{3}{8}$ -0.3

0 $|2|$

1.0205×10^{-23}

0.001 0.5%

20% 0.25

$\sqrt{0.25}$ $\sqrt{\frac{9}{16}}$

$0.\overline{91}$ $\sqrt{2}$

$1.523232323\ldots$

212% $|-3|$

π $6\frac{1}{4}$

$\frac{100}{11}$ $\sqrt{100}$

4^2 $627{,}513$

$1{,}000{,}872.0245$

3.21×10^{12}

TALK the TALK

Venn Diagrams and Real Numbers

Combining the set of rational numbers and the set of irrational numbers produces the set of **real numbers**. You can use a **Venn diagram** to represent how the sets within the set of real numbers are related.

1. **The Venn diagram shows the relationship between the six sets of numbers shown. Write each of the 30 numbers in the appropriate section of the Venn diagram.**

Real Numbers

Rational Numbers

Irrational Numbers

Integers

Whole Numbers

Natural Numbers

2. Use your Venn diagram to decide whether each statement is true or false. Explain your reasoning.

   a. A whole number is sometimes an irrational number.

   b. A real number is sometimes a rational number.

   c. A whole number is always an integer.

Assignment

Write

In your own words, write a definition for *irrational number*. Use examples to help illustrate your definition.

Remember

The set of real numbers includes the set of rational numbers and the set of irrational numbers.

Practice

1. Identify each number as rational or irrational.

   a. π

   b. $\sqrt{4}$

   c. $\sqrt{18}$

   d. $\sqrt[3]{27}$

   e. $\sqrt[3]{30}$

   f. $\frac{\sqrt{1}}{\sqrt{49}}$

2. Indicate whether each real number shown is a rational number, an irrational number, an integer, a whole number, a natural number, or some combination.

   a. 35

   b. $\sqrt{17}$

   c. -6

   d. 5.25

   e. $\sqrt{81}$

   f. $-\frac{2}{3}$

3. Consider the expressions $\sqrt{15}$, $\sqrt{97}$, and $\sqrt{40}$. Locate the approximate value of each on a number line. Then, estimate each square root to the nearest tenth.

Stretch

A number called the Champernowne constant is an irrational number formed by placing the digits of successive integers together, like this:

$$0.12345678910111213141516\ldots$$

What is the 100th digit of the Champernowne constant, not including the beginning zero?

Review

1. Write each repeating decimal as a fraction.

   a. 0.888...

   b. 0.272727...

2. Tell whether the system of equations has one solution, no solutions, or infinite solutions.

   a. $\begin{cases} y = 2x - 1 \\ y = 10 + 2x \end{cases}$

   b. $\begin{cases} 3x - y = -4 \\ y = 2(1.5x + 2) \end{cases}$

3. Solve each system of equations.

   a. $\begin{cases} 4x - 3y = 26 \\ x = 5y + 15 \end{cases}$

   b. $\begin{cases} 7x - 3y = -22 \\ 5x - 3y = -14 \end{cases}$

The Real Number System Summary

KEY TERMS

- natural numbers
- whole numbers
- integers
- closed
- rational numbers

- irrational numbers
- terminating decimal
- repeating decimal
- bar notation
- perfect cube

- cube root
- index
- real numbers
- Venn diagram

LESSON 1

So Many Numbers, So Little Time

Numbers can be grouped in a variety of ways according to their characteristics. Sometimes, a number may fit into multiple groupings. For example, $-\frac{3}{4}$ is both a fraction and a negative number. The number 27 can be grouped with whole numbers and with integers.

LESSON 2

Rational Decisions

The set of **natural numbers**, consists of the numbers that you use to count objects: {1, 2, 3, 4, 5, ...}. The set of **whole numbers** is made up of the set of natural numbers and the number 0, the additive identity. Another set of numbers is the set of **integers**, which is a set that includes all of the whole numbers and their additive inverses:
{..., −3, −2, −1, 0, 1, 2, 3, ...}

When you perform an operation such as addition or multiplication on the numbers in a set, the operation could produce a defined value that is also in the set. When this happens, the set is said to be **closed** under the operation. The set of integers is said to be closed under the operation of addition. This means that for every two integers a and b, the sum $a + b$ is also an integer.

A **rational number** is a number that can be written in the form $\frac{a}{b}$, where a and b are both integers and b is not equal to 0. A rational number can be written as either a terminating or repeating decimal. All other decimals are **irrational numbers**, because these decimals cannot be written as fractions in the form $\frac{a}{b}$, where a and b are integers and b is not equal to 0.

A **terminating decimal** is a decimal that has a finite number of non-zero digits $\left(\text{e.g.,} \frac{1}{8} = 0.125\right)$. A **repeating decimal** is a decimal with digits that repeat in sets of one or more. You can use two different notations to represent repeating decimals. One notation is **bar notation**, which shows one set of digits that repeats with a bar over the repeating digits $\left(\text{e.g.,} \frac{1}{3} = 0.\overline{3}\right)$. Another notation shows two sets of digits that repeat with dots to indicate repetition $\left(\text{e.g.,} \frac{1}{3} = 0.33...\right)$.

You can use algebra to determine the fraction that is represented by a repeating decimal.

For example, write the decimal 0.44... as a fraction.

$w = 0.44...$ First, write an equation by setting the decimal equal to a variable that will represent the fraction.

$10w = 4.4...$ Next, write another equation by multiplying both sides of the equation by a power of 10. The exponent on the power of 10 is equal to the number of decimal places until the decimal begins to repeat.

$10w = 4.44...$ Then, subtract the equations.
$\underline{-w = 0.44...}$
$9w = 4$

$w = \frac{4}{9}$ Finally, solve the equation by dividing both sides by 9.

A square root is one of two equal factors of a given number. Every positive number has two square roots: a positive square root and a negative square root. The positive square root is called the principal square root.

The symbol $\sqrt{10}$ is called a radical. The radicand is the quantity under a radical. For example, the expression shown is read as "the square root of 25," or as "radical 25."

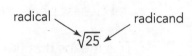

A perfect square is a number that is equal to the product of a distinct factor multiplied by itself. In the example above, 25 is a perfect square because it is equal to the product of 5 multiplied by itself.

The square roots of most numbers are not integers. You can estimate the square root of a number that is not a perfect square.

For example, to estimate $\sqrt{10}$ to the nearest tenth, identify the closest perfect square less than 10 and the closest perfect square greater than 10.

$$\sqrt{9} < \sqrt{10} < \sqrt{16}$$

This means that the estimate of $\sqrt{10}$ is between 3 and 4. Locate each square root on a number line. The approximate location of $\sqrt{10}$ is closer to 3 than to 4 when plotted.

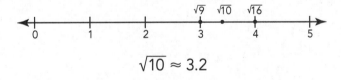

$$\sqrt{10} \approx 3.2$$

You can check your estimate by calculating the squares of values between 3 and 4.

$$(3.1)(3.1) = 9.61$$
$$(3.2)(3.2) = 10.24$$
$$(3.3)(3.3) = 10.89$$

A **perfect cube** is the cube of a whole number. For example, 64 is a perfect cube since 4 is a whole number and $4 \times 4 \times 4 = 64$. A **cube root** is one of 3 equal factors of a number. As with the square root, the cube root also uses a radical symbol but has a 3 as an index: $\sqrt[3]{1}$. The **index** is the number placed above and to the left of the radical to indicate what root is being calculated.

$$\sqrt[3]{27} < \sqrt[3]{33} < \sqrt[3]{64}$$

You can use the same method used to estimate the square root of a number to estimate the cube root of a number.

> To estimate $\sqrt[3]{33}$ to the nearest tenth, identify the closest perfect cube less than 33 and the closest perfect cube greater than 33.

> This means that the estimate of $\sqrt[3]{33}$ is between 3 and 4. Locate the approximate value of $\sqrt[3]{33}$ on a number line.

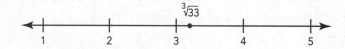

> Next, choose decimals between 3 and 4, and calculate the cube of each decimal to determine which one is the best estimate.

> Consider: $(3.2)(3.2)(3.2) = 32.768$
> $(3.3)(3.3)(3.3) = 35.937$

> Therefore, $\sqrt[3]{33} \approx 3.2$.

Pythagorean Theorem

James Abram Garfield was the 20th President of the United States. Garfield also discovered a unique proof of the Pythagorean Theorem.

Module 4: Expanding Number Systems

TOPIC 2: PYTHAGOREAN THEOREM

In this topic, students explore the Pythagorean Theorem and its converse. They learn that in the case of right triangles, knowing two side lengths allows them to determine the third side length, therefore forming a unique triangle. Students practice applying the theorem to determine unknown side lengths in right triangles and apply the converse of the theorem: if three side lengths are given, determine if the triangle is a right triangle. Students apply the Pythagorean Theorem to real-world and mathematical problems.

Where have we been?

Students learned about right angles and right triangles in grade 4 and evaluated numerical expressions with whole-number exponents in grade 6, and they have continued to use these skills in subsequent courses.

Where are we going?

In high school, students will use right triangles and similarity to define ratios of sides, the trigonometric ratios. These new ratios, along with the Pythagorean Theorem, will be used to solve application problems. Students will use the Pythagorean Theorem in the study of analytic geometry when they use coordinates to prove geometric theorems algebraically, including deriving the Distance Formula.

Studying Visual Proofs of the Pythagorean Theorem

The triangles on the left, with leg lengths a and b and hypotenuse length c, can be rearranged as shown on the right. The space not occupied by the triangles in each figure is equal to $a^2 + b^2$ (on the left) and c^2 (on the right), proving that $a^2 + b^2 = c^2$, which is the Pythagorean Theorem.

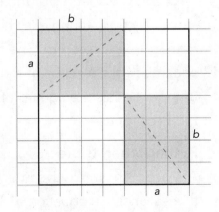
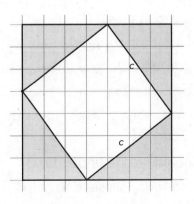

Myth: "I'm not smart."

The word "smart" is tricky because it means different things to different people. For example, would you say a baby is "smart"? On the one hand, a baby is helpless and doesn't know anything. But on the other hand, a baby is exceptionally smart because they are constantly learning new things every day.

This example is meant to demonstrate that "smart" can have two meanings. It can mean "the knowledge that you have," or it can mean, "the capacity to learn from experience." When someone says they are "not smart," are they saying they do not have lots of knowledge, or are they saying they lack the capacity to learn? If it's the first definition, then none of us are smart until we acquire that information. If it's the second definition, then we know that is completely untrue because everyone has the capacity to grow as a result of new experiences.

So, if your student doesn't think that they are smart, encourage them to be patient. They have the capacity to learn new facts and skills. It might not be easy, and it will take some time and effort. But the brain is automatically wired to learn. Smart should not refer only to how much knowledge you currently have.

#mathmythbusted

Talking Points

You can further support your student's learning by asking questions about the work they do in class or at home. Your student is learning about the Pythagorean Theorem.

Questions to Ask

- How does this problem look like something you did in class?
- Can you show me the strategy you used to solve this problem? Do you know another way to solve it?
- Does your answer make sense? How do you know?
- Is there anything you don't understand? How can you use today's lesson to help?

Key Terms

hypotenuse
The side opposite the right angle in a right triangle is called the hypotenuse. The other two sides are called legs of the right triangle.

Pythagorean Theorem
The special relationship that exists between the squares of the lengths of the sides of a right triangle is known as the Pythagorean Theorem. The sum of the squares of the lengths of the legs of a right triangle equals the square of the length of the hypotenuse: $a^2 + b^2 = c^2$.

Pythagorean triple
Any set of three positive integers a, b, and c that satisfies the equation $a^2 + b^2 = c^2$ is a Pythagorean triple.

The Right Triangle Connection

The Pythagorean Theorem

WARM UP

Solve for x.

1. $8^2 + 3^2 = x^2$

2. $36 + x^2 = 85$

3. $3^2 + 4^2 = x^2$

4. $6^2 + 8^2 = x^2$

LEARNING GOALS

- Make and prove a conjecture about the relationship between the lengths of the sides of right triangles.
- Explain a proof of the Pythagorean Theorem.
- Use the Pythagorean Theorem to determine the unknown side lengths in right triangles.

KEY TERMS

- hypotenuse
- legs
- Pythagorean Theorem
- proof
- diagonal of a square

You know the sum of two side lengths of any triangle is greater than the length of the third side. Are there other relationships between the side lengths of a triangle? What special relationships exist between the side lengths of a right triangle?

Searching for the Right Pattern

The triangles are not drawn to scale.

A right triangle is a triangle with a right angle. A right angle has a measure of 90° and is indicated by a square drawn at the corner formed by the angle.

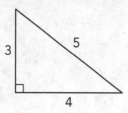
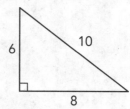
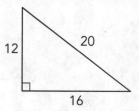

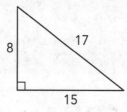
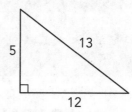
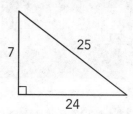

If you square the length of each side of the first triangle, you get

$$3^2 = 9 \qquad 4^2 = 16 \qquad 5^2 = 25.$$

If you repeat this process with the second triangle, you get

$$6^2 = 36 \qquad 8^2 = 64 \qquad 10^2 = 100.$$

1. **Repeat this process with the remaining triangles. Do you see a pattern in the squares of the side lengths of a right triangle? If so, describe it.**

Introducing the Pythagorean Theorem

In the right triangle shown, the lengths of the sides are a, b, and c.

1. **Using the pattern you discovered in the previous activity, what statement can you make about the relationship among a^2, b^2, and c^2?**

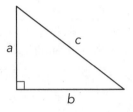

2. **Consider the relative lengths of the sides of the triangle.**

   a. **Which side length must be the longest: a, b, or c? Explain how you know.**

   b. **Describe the relationship between the side lengths of any triangle.**

The side opposite the right angle in a right triangle is called the **hypotenuse**. The other two sides are called **legs** of the right triangle. In the figure, the sides with lengths a and b are the legs, and the side with length c is the hypotenuse.

3. **Label the legs and the hypotenuse in the right triangle shown.**

The special relationship that exists between the squares of the lengths of the sides of a right triangle is known as the *Pythagorean Theorem*. The **Pythagorean Theorem** states that the sum of the squares of the lengths of the legs of a right triangle equals the square of the length of the hypotenuse.

$$a^2 + b^2 = c^2$$

The Pythagorean Theorem is one of the earliest known theorems to ancient civilization and one of the most famous. This theorem was named after Pythagoras (580 to 496 B.C.), a Greek mathematician and and philosopher who was the first to prove the theorem.

You can verify that the Pythagorean Theorem holds true for the triangles in the previous activity.

> **WORKED EXAMPLE**
>
> The first right triangle has sides of length 3 units, 4 units, and 5 units, where the sides of length 3 units and 4 units are the legs and the side with length 5 units is the hypotenuse.
>
> The sum of the squares of the
> lengths of the legs: $\qquad 3^2 + 4^2 = 9 + 16$
> $= 25$
> The square of the hypotenuse: $5^2 = 25$
>
> Therefore $3^2 + 4^2 = 5^2$, which verifies the Pythagorean Theorem, holds true.

The sum of the lengths of two sides of a triangle must be greater than the length of the third side.

---

4. **Verify that the Pythagorean Theorem holds true for two additional triangles.**

   a. **right triangle with side lengths 8, 15, and 17**

   b. **right triangle with side lengths 7, 24, and 25**

5. **Use the Pythagorean Theorem to determine the length of the hypotenuse in each right triangle. Round your answer to the nearest tenth, if necessary.**

   a.
   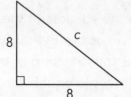

   b.
   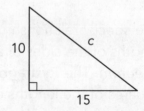

Proving the Pythagorean Theorem

You verified the Pythagorean Theorem for select triangles, but how do you know that it holds for *all* right triangles? In this activity, you will create a geometric *proof* of the theorem.

A **proof** is a line of reasoning used to validate a theorem.

1. **Complete the geometric proof assigned to you. The cut-outs for proofs are located at the end of the lesson. Then record your findings on the graphic organizer and prepare to share your results with your classmates.**

Proof 1
An isosceles right triangle is drawn on the grid.

a. **A square on the hypotenuse has been drawn for you. Use a straightedge to draw squares on the other two sides of the triangle. Then use different colored pencils to shade each small square.**

b. **Draw two diagonals in each of the two smaller squares.**

c. **Cut out the two smaller squares along the legs. Then, cut those squares into fourths along the diagonals you drew.**

d. **Redraw your original figure and the squares on the grid on the graphic organizer at the end of the activity. Shade the smaller squares again.**

A **diagonal of a square** is a line segment connecting opposite vertices of the square.

e. **Arrange the pieces that you cut out to fit inside the larger square on the graphic organizer. Then, tape the triangles on top of the larger square.**

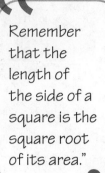

Remember that the length of the side of a square is the square root of its area."

Proof 2

A right triangle has one leg 4 units in length and the other leg 3 units in length.

a. Use a straightedge to draw squares on each side of the triangle. Use different colored pencils to shade each square along the legs.

b. Cut out the two smaller squares along the legs.

c. Cut the two squares into strips that are either 4 units by 1 unit or 3 units by 1 unit.

d. Redraw your original figure and the squares on the grid on the graphic organizer at the end of the activity. Shade the smaller squares again.

e. Arrange the strips and squares you cut out on top of the square along the hypotenuse on the graphic organizer. You may need to make additional cuts to the strips to create individual squares that are 1 unit by 1 unit. Then, tape the strips on top of the square you drew on the hypotenuse.

Proof 3

A right triangle has one leg 2 units in length and the other leg 4 units in length.

a. Use a straightedge to draw squares on each side of the triangle. Use different colored pencils to shade each square along the legs.

b. Cut out the two smaller squares.

c. Draw four congruent right triangles on the square with side lengths of 4 units. Then, cut out the four congruent right triangles you drew.

d. Redraw your original figure and the squares on the grid on the graphic organizer at the end of the activity. Shade the smaller squares again.

e. Arrange and tape the small square and the 4 congruent triangles you cut out over the square that has one of its sides as the hypotenuse.

Description of Right Triangle in Proof

What do you
notice?

Describe the
relationship
among the areas of
the squares.

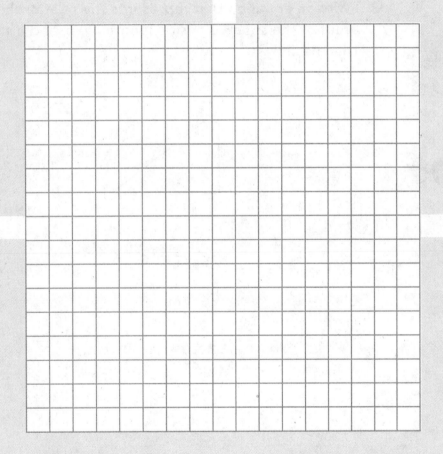

Determine the length of the hypotenuse.

Share your proof and graphic organizer with your classmates.

2. Compare the descriptions of the relationship among the areas of the squares from each proof. What do you notice?

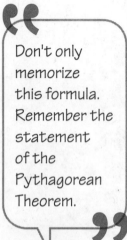

Don't only memorize this formula. Remember the statement of the Pythagorean Theorem.

3. Write an equation that represents the relationship among the areas of the squares of side lengths *a*, *b*, and *c* in the right triangle shown.

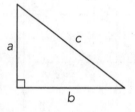

Determining the Length of the Hypotenuse

The Pythagorean Theorem can be used to determine unknown side lengths in a right triangle. Evan and Sophi are using the theorem to determine the length of the hypotenuse, c, with leg lengths of 2 and 4. Examine their work.

Evan

$$c^2 = 2^2 + 4^2$$
$$c^2 = 6^2$$
$$c = 6$$

The length of the hypotenuse is 6 units.

Sophi

$$c^2 = 2^2 + 4^2$$
$$c^2 = 4 + 16 = 20$$
$$c = \sqrt{20} \approx 4.5$$

The length of the hypotenuse is approximately 4.5 units.

1. Explain the algebraic error in Evan's work.

Mitch maintains the Magnolia Middle School campus. Use the Pythagorean Theorem to help Mitch with some of his jobs.

2. Mitch needs to wash the windows on the second floor of a building. He knows the windows are 12 feet above the ground. Because of dense shrubbery, he has to put the base of the ladder 5 feet from the building. What ladder length does he need?

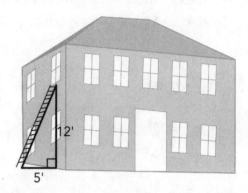

3. The gym teacher, Ms. Fisher, asked Mitch to put up the badminton net. Ms. Fisher said that the top of the net must be 5 feet above the ground. She knows that Mitch will need to put stakes in the ground for rope supports. She asked that the stakes be placed 6 feet from the base of the poles. Mitch has two pieces of rope, one that is 7 feet long and a second that is 8 feet long. Will these two pieces of rope be enough to secure the badminton poles? Explain your reasoning.

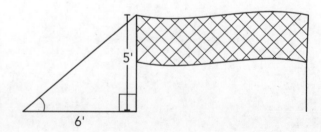

4. Mitch stopped by the baseball field to watch the team practice. The first baseman caught a line drive right on the base. He touched first base for one out and quickly threw the ball to third base to get another out. How far did he throw the ball?

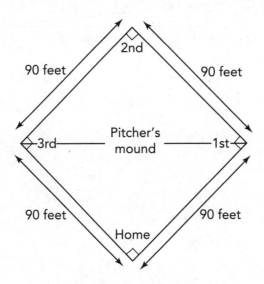

5. The skate ramp on the playground of a neighboring park is going to be replaced. Mitch needs to determine how long the ramp is to get estimates on the cost of a new skate ramp. He knows the measurements shown in the figure. How long is the existing skate ramp?

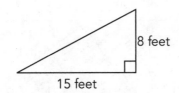

6. A wheelchair ramp that is constructed to rise 1 foot off the ground must extend 12 feet along the ground. How long will the wheelchair ramp be?

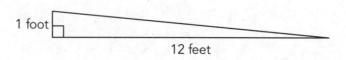

7. The school's new industrial-size refrigerator is 7 feet tall and 5 feet wide. The refrigerator is lying on its side. Mitch and the movers want to tilt the refrigerator upright, but they are worried that the refrigerator might hit the 8-foot ceiling. Will the refrigerator hit the ceiling when it is tilted upright?

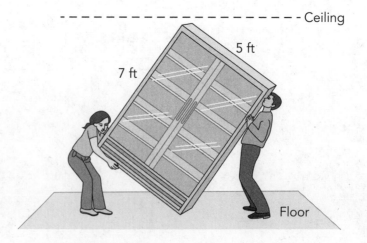

Use the Pythagorean Theorem to solve each problem.

1. Write an equation to determine each unknown length.
   Then, solve the equation. Round your answer to the nearest
   tenth, if necessary.

a.

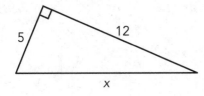

b.

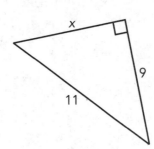

c.

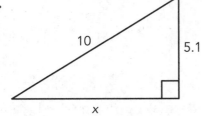

d.

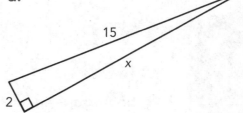

Would it help to draw a picture?

2. Chandra has a ladder that is 20 feet long. If the top of the ladder reaches 16 feet up the side of a building, how far from the building is the base of the ladder?

3. The length of the hypotenuse of a right triangle is 40 centimeters. The legs of the triangle are the same length. How long is each leg of the triangle?

What path will the plane take to reach the runway?

4. A plane is 5 miles directly above a house and 42 miles from the runway at the nearest airport. How far is the house from the airport?

5. A boat drops an anchor at the deepest point of the lake and spends the day drifting along the lake. If the lake is 75 feet deep and the chain on the anchor is 200 feet, determine the greatest distance the boat can drift from where it dropped anchor.

TALK the TALK

Another Proof!

While it is called the Pythagorean Theorem, the mathematical knowledge was used by the Babylonians 1000 years before Pythagoras. Many proofs followed that of Pythagoras, including ones proved by Euclid, Socrates, and even the twentieth President of the United States, President James A. Garfield.

Let's use the figures shown to prove the Pythagorean Theorem another way. Each figure includes four right triangles with leg lengths *a* and *b* and hypotenuse of length *c*.

Figure 1   Figure 2

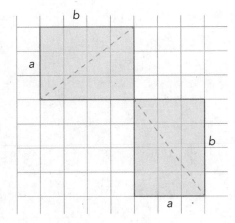   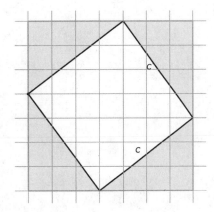

1. **Write an expression for the total area of the non-shaded region of Figure 1, in terms of *a* and *b*.**

2. Explain how to use transformations to transform Figure 1 onto Figure 2.

3. Write an expression for the non-shaded region of Figure 2, in terms of *c*.

4. Explain why these figures prove the Pythagorean Theorem.

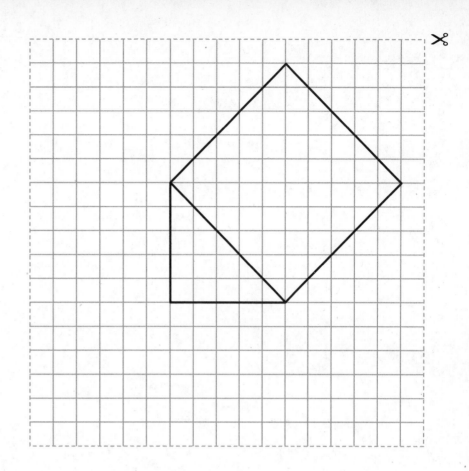

Proof 2

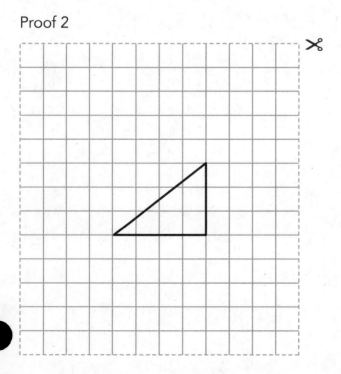

Proof 3

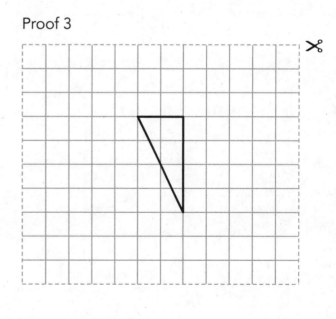

Assignment

Practice

Determine the unknown in each situation. Round your answers to the nearest tenth.

1. Lamar goes shopping for a new flat-panel television. A television is usually described by the length of the screen's diagonal. He finds a great deal on a 42-inch display model.
   a. If the screen's height is 21 inches, what is the width of the screen?
   b. The border around the screen is 2 inches. What are the dimensions of the television, including the border?
   c. How long is the diagonal of the television, including the border?

2. Lamar sells his old television in his neighborhood's garage sale. It has a rectangular screen with a diagonal measure of 27 inches. A potential buyer is concerned about the television fitting in the 24-inch square opening of his entertainment center.

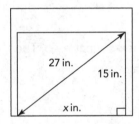

   a. What is the width of the television's screen?
   b. Will the television fit in the buyer's entertainment center? Explain your reasoning.

3. Clayton is responsible for changing the broken light bulb in a streetlamp. The streetlamp is 12 feet high. Clayton places the base of his ladder 4 feet from the base of the streetlamp. Clayton can extend his ladder from 10 feet to 14 feet. How long must his ladder be to reach the top of the streetlamp?

4. A scaffold has a diagonal support beam to strengthen it. If the scaffold is 15 feet high and 5 feet wide, how long must the support beam be?

5. A rectangular swimming pool is 24 meters by 10 meters. Jane said she could swim diagonally from one corner to another without taking a breath. Carli said she could swim much farther than Jane and still swim diagonally from one corner to another. Determine the distances Jane and Carli may have swum.

Determine the unknown side length in each right triangle. Round your answers to the nearest tenth.

6.

7.

8.

9.

10.

11.

Stretch

Examine President Garfield's proof of the Pythagorean Theorem.

In the figure, an arbitrary right triangle with sides of length a and b and hypotenuse of length c was drawn and copied so that $a \parallel b$. Then, an additional segment was drawn to form a trapezoid.

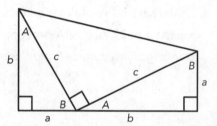

1. Determine the area of the trapezoid using the formula, $A = \frac{1}{2}(b_1 + b_2)h$, where b_1 and b_2 are the lengths of the parallel bases and h is the perpendicular distance between the bases.

2. Determine the area of each triangle inside the trapezoid. Sum the areas.

3. How do these area calculations prove the Pythagorean Theorem? (Hint: $(a + b)^2 = a^2 + 2ab + b^2$.)

Review

1. Estimate each radical to the nearest tenth.
   a. $\sqrt{38}$ b. $\sqrt{14}$

2. Name all number sets to which each number belongs.
   a. $\frac{2}{3}$ b. 5

3. Solve each equation.
   a. $4x + 3x + 12 = 2(15 + 2x)$ b. $3(2c + 5) = 12 + 3(c + 4)$

Can That Be Right? **2**

The Converse of the Pythagorean Theorem

WARM UP
A bird leaves its nest and flies 3 miles due south, 2 miles due east, 5 miles due south, and 1 mile due east to visit a friend's nest.

1. Draw a model of the situation.
2. Determine the distance between the nests.

LEARNING GOALS
- Determine if three side lengths form a right triangle.
- Generate side lengths of right triangles.
- Use the Pythagorean Theorem and the Converse of the Pythagorean Theorem to determine unknown side lengths in right triangles.

KEY TERMS
- converse
- Converse of the Pythagorean Theorem
- Pythagorean triple

You know that the Pythagorean Theorem can be used to solve for unknown lengths in a right triangle. How can you use the theorem to prove that a triangle is a right triangle?

Is It Right?

Often, geometry diagrams are not drawn to scale, and even if a triangle looks like a right triangle, it may not be. A square is used to indicate the presence of the right angle, but what if that symbol is missing? How do you know if a triangle is a right triangle?

1. **Use a protractor to determine which triangles are right triangles.**

a.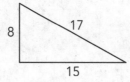

b.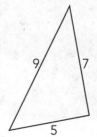

c.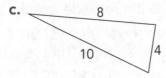

d.

> Does a non-right triangle have a hypotenuse?

2. **What do you notice about the squares of the lengths of the sides of the triangle of the non-right triangles versus the right triangles?**

The Pythagorean Theorem can be used to solve many problems involving right triangles, squares, and rectangles. The Pythagorean Theorem states that, if a triangle is a right triangle, then the square of the hypotenuse length equals the sum of the squares of the leg lengths. Have you wondered if the *converse* is true?

The **Converse of the Pythagorean Theorem** states that if the sum of the squares of the two shorter sides of a triangle equals the square of the longest side, then the triangle is a right triangle.

In other words, if the lengths of the sides of a triangle satisfy the equation $a^2 + b^2 = c^2$, then the triangle is a right triangle.

The **converse** of a theorem is created when the if-then parts of that theorem are exchanged.

---

1. **Determine whether the triangle with the given side lengths is a right triangle.**

   a. 9, 12, 15   b. 24, 45, 51

   c. 25, 16, 9   d. 8, 8, 11

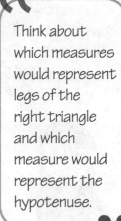

Think about which measures would represent legs of the right triangle and which measure would represent the hypotenuse.

You may have noticed that each of the right triangles in Question 1 had side lengths that were integers. Any set of three positive integers a, b, and c that satisfies the equation $a^2 + b^2 = c^2$ is a **Pythagorean triple**. For example, the integers 3, 4, and 5 form a Pythagorean triple because $3^2 + 4^2 = 5^2$.

Given a Pythagorean triple, you can identify other right triangles by multiplying each side length by the same factor.

2. **Complete the table to identify more Pythagorean triples.**

	a	b	c	Check: $a^2 + b^2 = c^2$
Pythagorean Triple	3	4	5	9 + 16 = 25
Multiply by 2				
Multiply by 3				
Multiply by 5				

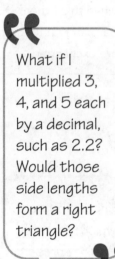

What if I multiplied 3, 4, and 5 each by a decimal, such as 2.2? Would those side lengths form a right triangle?

3. **Determine a new Pythagorean triple not used in Question 2, and complete the table.**

	a	b	c	Check: $a^2 + b^2 = c^2$
Pythagorean Triple				
Multiply by 2				
Multiply by 3				
Multiply by 5				

4. **Record other Pythagorean triples that your classmates determined.**

Proving the Converse

Because the Converse of the Pythagorean Theorem is, itself, a theorem, you can prove it.

Step 1: Assume you are given $\triangle ABC$ such that the sum of the squares of the lengths of two sides equals the square of the length of the third side, or $a^2 + b^2 = c^2$.

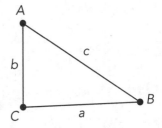

1. Do you have enough information to determine if the triangle is a right triangle without using the Converse of the Pythagorean Theorem? Why can't you use the converse to answer this question?

Step 2: Now, construct a right triangle, $\triangle DEF$, using the side lengths a and b from Triangle ABC. By the Pythagorean Theorem, $a^2 + b^2 = x^2$, where x is the hypotenuse of $\triangle DEF$.

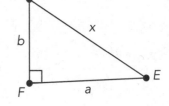

2. Why can you apply the Pythagorean Theorem to the side lengths of $\triangle DEF$?

Step 3: If $a^2 + b^2 = c^2$ and $a^2 + b^2 = x^2$, then $c^2 = x^2$ and $c = x$.

3. Explain why $c^2 = x^2$.

Recall that three sides of a triangle create a unique triangle. Therefore, all triangles with those side lengths are congruent.

Step 4: $\triangle ABC \cong \triangle DEF$ because all of their corresponding side lengths are equal.

4. If the triangles are congruent and $\triangle DEF$ is a right triangle, what must be true about $\triangle ABC$?

You have proven the Converse of the Pythagorean Theorem. If the sum of the squares of the lengths of two sides of a triangle equals the square of the length of the third side, then the triangle is a right triangle.

ACTIVITY
2.3   Applying the Theorems

Use your knowledge of the Pythagorean Theorem and its converse to solve each.

1. A carpenter attaches a brace to a rectangular picture frame. If the dimensions of the picture frame are 30 inches by 40 inches, what is the length of the brace?

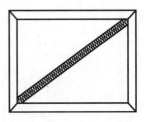

2. Bill is staking out a location to build a rectangular deck that will be 8 feet wide and 15 feet long. Tyrone is helping Bill with the deck. Tyrone has two boards, one that is 8 feet long and one that is 7 feet long. He puts the two boards together, end to end, and lays them on the diagonal of the deck area, where they just fit. What should he tell Bill?

3. A television is identified by the diagonal measurement of the screen. A television has a 36-inch screen, whose height is 22 inches. What is the width of the television screen? Round your answer to the nearest inch.

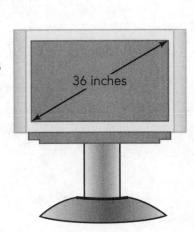

4. Orville and Jerri want to put a custom-made, round table in their dining room. The table top is made of glass with a diameter of 85 inches. The front door is 36 inches wide and 80 inches tall. Orville thinks the table top will fit through the door, but Jerri does not. Who is correct and why?

5. Sherie makes a canvas frame for a painting using stretcher bars. The rectangular painting will be 12 inches long and 9 inches wide. How can she use a ruler to make sure that the corners of the frame will be right angles?

6. A 10-foot ladder is placed 4 feet from the edge of a building. How far up the building does the ladder reach? Round your answer to the nearest tenth of a foot.

7. Chris has a tent that is 64 inches wide with a slant height of 68 inches on each side. What is the height of the center pole needed to prop up the tent?

8. A ship left shore and sailed 240 kilometers east, turned due north, and then sailed another 70 kilometers. How many kilometers is the ship from shore by the most direct path?

9. Danielle walks 88 feet due east to the library from her house. From the library, she walks 187 feet northwest to the corner store. Finally, she walks approximately 139 feet from the corner store back home. Does she live directly south of the corner store? Justify your answer.

10. What is the diagonal length of a square that has a side length of 10 cm?

TALK the TALK

Triple Play

Create a Pythagorean triple that contains each length or lengths. Verify that the side lengths form a right triangle.

1. 9 and 41

2. 21 and 29

3. 12

4. 15

5. Can any integer be used to create a Pythagorean triple? Why or why not?

6. Are the side lengths of a right triangle always integers? Why or why not?

Assignment

Write

Complete each statement:

1. The Converse of the Pythagorean Theorem states that if the sum of the squares of two sides of a triangle equals the square of the third side, then the triangle is a _____.

2. The converse of a theorem is created when the if-then parts of the theorem are _____.

3. A Pythagorean triple is a set of three _____ _____ a, b, and c that satisfy the equation $a^2 + b^2 = c^2$.

Remember

The Converse of the Pythagorean Theorem is used to determine if triangles are right triangles.

Practice

1. Determine whether each triangle with the given side lengths is a right triangle.

   a. 6, 9, 14

   b. 2, 3.75, 4.25

   c.
   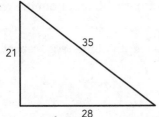

   d.
   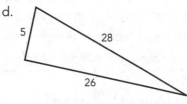

2. Elena has received grant money to open a local community center. She wants to save as much of the money as possible for programs. She will be doing many of the improvements herself to the old building she has rented. While touring the building to make her project list, she uses a tape measure to check whether floors, doorways, and walls are square, meaning that they meet at right angles.

   a. Elena measures the lobby of the building for new laminate flooring. The length is 30 feet, the width is 16 feet, and the diagonal is 34 feet. Is the room square?

   b. Can Elena use the edges of the room as a guide to start laying the boards of laminate flooring? Explain your reasoning.

   c. The landing outside the main entrance of the building does not have a railing. Elena wants to install railing around the landing to make it safer. The length of the landing is 12 feet, the width is 9 feet, and the diagonal is 14 feet. Is the landing square?

   d. Elena needs to order a new door for her office. The width of the door frame is 3 feet, the height is 8 feet, and the diagonal is $8\frac{5}{8}$ feet. Is the door frame square?

   e. The sign that will be mounted to the outside of the building is a rectangle that is 9 feet by 12 feet. The largest doorway into the building is 4 feet wide and 8 feet high. What is the diagonal measurement of the doorway?

   f. Does Elena have to mount the sign the day it is delivered or can she store it inside the building until she is ready? Explain your answer.

3. Given the Pythagorean triple 21-220-221, generate an additional triple and verify that the side lengths form a right triangle.

Stretch

Euclid developed a formula for generating Pythagorean triples given any integers m and n with $m > n > 0$: $a = m^2 - n^2$, $b = 2mn$, and $c = m^2 + n^2$.

It can be proven that there are exactly eight Pythagorean triples for a right triangle with a perimeter of 840 units.

Use Euclid's formula, your knowledge of perimeter and algebra, and number sense to find as many of the eight Pythagorean triples with a perimeter of 840 units as you can.

Review

1. A carpenter props a ladder against the wall of a building. The base of the ladder is 10 feet from the wall. The top of the ladder is 24 feet from the ground. How long is the ladder?

2. The length of the hypotenuse of a right triangle is 50 inches. Determine the length of the legs if each leg is the same length.

3. Rewrite each repeating decimal as a fraction.

   a. 0.191919...   b. $0.\overline{5}$

4. Solve each system of equations.

   a. $\begin{cases} y = 4x + 3 \\ y = 2x + 5 \end{cases}$ b. $\begin{cases} 3x + y = 14 \\ y = 5x - 2 \end{cases}$

Pythagoras Meets Descartes

3

Distances in a Coordinate System

WARM UP

Use the coordinate plane shown to answer each question.

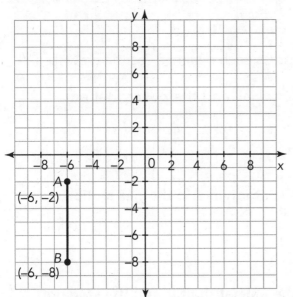

1. How do you calculate the distance between points *A* and *B*?

2. What is the distance between points *A* and *B*?

3. How do the negative coordinates affect the distance between points *A* and *B*?

LEARNING GOALS

- Apply the Pythagorean Theorem to determine the distance between two points on a coordinate plane.
- Use square roots to represent solutions to equations.

You have learned about the Pythagorean Theorem and the Converse of the Pythagorean Theorem. How can you apply the Pythagorean Theorem to determine distances on a coordinate plane?

As the Crow Flies

The map shows certain locations within a city. Each unit on the map represents 1 block.

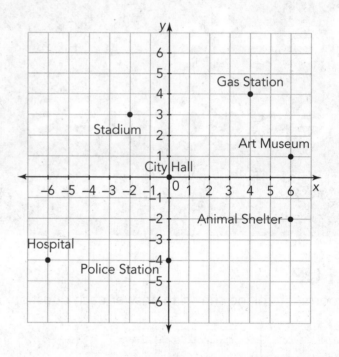

The phrase *as the crow flies* means "the straight-line distance" between two points.

Describe how you could express each distance "as the crow flies."

1. **the distance between City Hall and the police station**

2. **the distance between the stadium and the gas station**

3. **the distance between the animal shelter and the stadium**

Right Triangles on the Coordinate Plane

Two friends, Shawn and Tamara, live in a city in which the streets are laid out in a grid system.

Shawn lives on Descartes Avenue and Tamara lives on Pythagoras Street, as shown.

1. **The two friends often meet at the bookstore. Each grid square represents one city block.**

   a. **How many blocks does Shawn walk to get to the bookstore?**

   b. **How many blocks does Tamara walk to get to the bookstore?**

   c. **Determine the distance, in blocks, Tamara would walk if she traveled from her house to the bookstore and then to Shawn's house.**

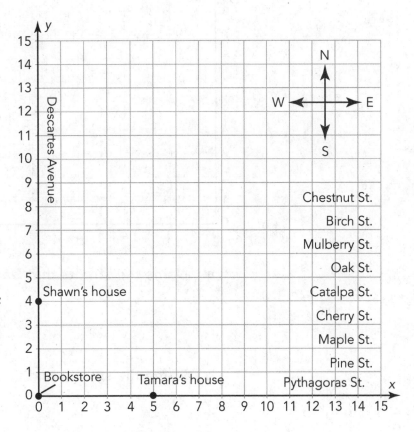

   d. **Determine the distance, in blocks, Tamara would walk if she traveled in a straight line from her house to Shawn's house. Explain your calculation. Round your answer to the nearest tenth of a block.**

2. **Don, a friend of Shawn and Tamara, lives three blocks east of Descartes Avenue and five blocks north of Pythagoras Street. Freda, another friend, lives seven blocks east of Descartes Avenue and two blocks north of Pythagoras Street. Plot the location of Don's house and Freda's house on the grid. Label each location and label the coordinates of each location.**

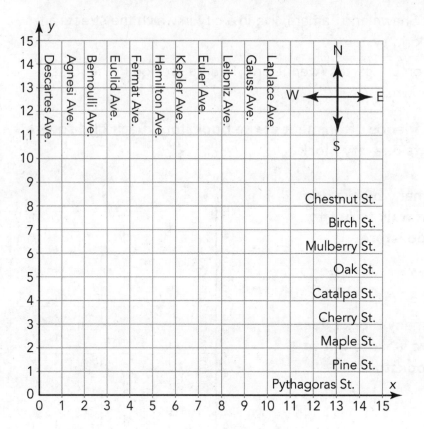

a. Name the streets that Don lives on.

b. Name the streets that Freda lives on.

3. Another friend, Bert, lives at the intersection of the avenue that Don lives on and the street that Freda lives on. Plot the location of Bert's house on the grid in Question 2 and label the coordinates. Describe the location of Bert's house with respect to Descartes Avenue and Pythagoras Street.

4. How do the coordinates of Bert's house compare to the coordinates of Don's house and Freda's house?

5. Use ordered pairs to write and evaluate an expression that represents the distance between Don's and Bert's houses.

6. How far, in blocks, does Don have to walk to get to Bert's house?

7. Use ordered pairs to write an expression that represents the distance between Bert's and Freda's houses.

8. How far, in blocks, does Bert have to walk to get to Freda's house?

9. All three friends meet at Don's house to study geometry. Freda walks to Bert's house, and then they walk together to Don's house. Use the coordinates to write and evaluate an expression that represents the distance from Freda's house to Bert's house, and from Bert's house to Don's house.

10. How far, in blocks, does Freda walk altogether?

11. Draw the direct path from Don's house to Freda's house on the coordinate plane in Question 2. If Freda walks to Don's house on this path, how far, in blocks, does she walk? Explain how you determined your answer.

Applying the Pythagorean Theorem to Determine Distances on the Coordinate Plane

The points (1, 2) and (3, 7) are shown on the coordinate plane. You can calculate the distance between these two points by drawing a right triangle. When you think about this line segment as the hypotenuse of the right triangle, you can use the Pythagorean Theorem.

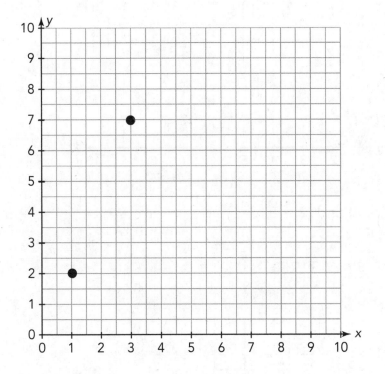

1. **Calculate the distance between the two points shown.**

   a. **Connect the points with a line segment. Draw a right triangle with this line segment as the hypotenuse.**

   b. **Determine the lengths of each leg of the right triangle. Then use the Pythagorean Theorem to determine the length of the hypotenuse. Round your answer to the nearest tenth.**

> Therefore, if you think of the distance between two points as a hypotenuse, you can draw a right triangle and then use the Pythagorean Theorem to calculate its length.

2. Determine the distance between each pair of points. Round your answer to the nearest tenth.

a. (3, 4) and (6, 8)

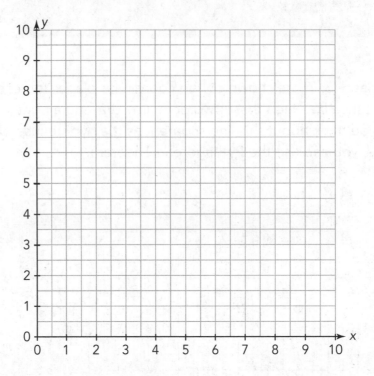

b. (−6, 4) and (2, −8)

Make sure to pay attention to the intervals shown on the axes.

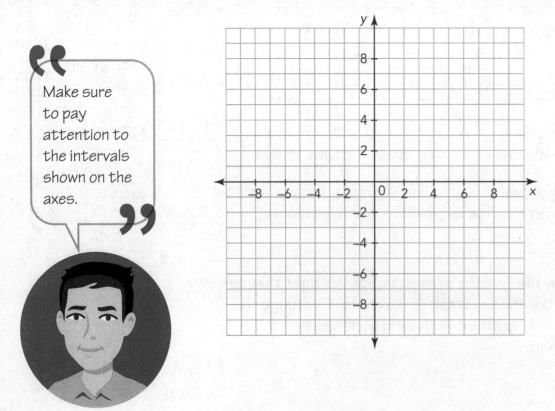

c. (−5, 2) and (−6, 10)

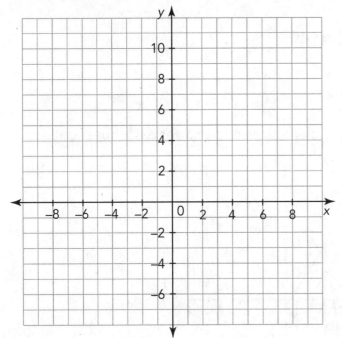

d. (−1, −4) and (−3, −6)

TALK the TALK

Exit Ticket

Use the coordinate plane shown to answer each question.

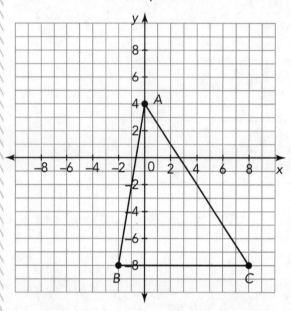

1. **What are the coordinates of the vertices of △ABC?**

2. **What is a strategy for determining the length of side AC?**

3. **Determine the length of side AC.**

4. **Can the same strategy be used to determine the length of side AB?**

5. **Determine the length of side AB.**

Assignment

Write

In your own words, explain how to determine the distance between two points on a coordinate plane when the points:

(a) have the same y-coordinate.

(b) have the same x-coordinate.

(c) have different x- and y-coordinates.

Remember

The distance between two points on a coordinate plane is always a positive number.

Practice

1. Ben is playing soccer with his friends Abby and Clay. The grid shows their locations on the soccer field. Each grid square represents a square that is 2 meters long and 2 meters wide. How far does Ben have to kick the ball to reach Clay?

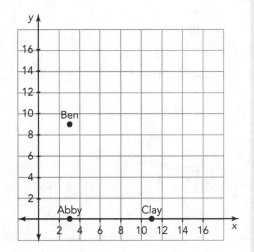

2. Graph and connect each pair of points on a coordinate plane. Then calculate the distance between each pair of points.

   a. $(-8, 3)$ and $(-8, 9)$

   b. $(-6, 8)$ and $(-1, 8)$

   c. $(8, -7)$ and $(-4, -7)$

   d. $(8, 8)$ and $(8, -2)$

3. Calculate the distances between the points.

   a. $(4, 1)$, $(2, 1)$, and $(4, 4)$

   b. $(1, -4)$, $(1, 1)$, and $(-2, -4)$

Stretch
What right triangles can be drawn, given the coordinates of the endpoints of the hypotenuse (−1, 1) and (2, 5)?

Review
1. Determine whether the triangle with the given side lengths is a right triangle.

   a. 105, 175, 140

   b. 36, 49, 64

2. Determine whether each number is rational or irrational.

   a. $-\frac{1}{6}$

   b. $\sqrt{81}$

   c. $\sqrt[3]{19}$

   d. $\sqrt[3]{100}$

3. Solve each equation.

   a. $4x^2 = 100$

   b. $x^3 - 10 = -2$

Catty Corner

Side Lengths in Two and Three Dimensions

WARM UP

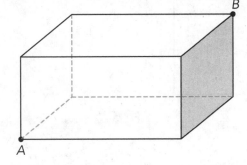

1. Imagine that the rectangular solid is a room. An ant is on the floor situated at point *A*. Describe the shortest path the ant can crawl to get to point *B* in the corner of the ceiling.

2. Suppose it isn't really an ant at all—it's a fly! Describe the shortest path the fly can fly to get from point *A* to point *B*.

3. If the ant's path and the fly's path were connected, what figure would they form?

LEARNING GOALS

- Apply the Pythagorean Theorem to determine unknown side lengths of right triangles in mathematical and real-world problems.
- Apply the Pythagorean Theorem to determine the lengths of diagonals of two- and three-dimensional figures.

KEY TERM

- diagonal

You have learned about the Pythagorean Theorem and its converse. How can you apply the Pythagorean Theorem to determine lengths in geometric figures?

Diagonally

Draw all of the sides you cannot see in each rectangular solid using dotted lines. Then draw a three-dimensional diagonal using a solid line.

1.
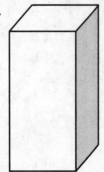

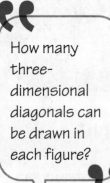
How many three-dimensional diagonals can be drawn in each figure?

2.
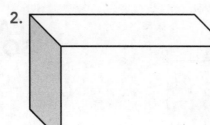

Determining the Lengths of Diagonals of Rectangles and Trapezoids

Previously, you have drawn or created many right triangles and used the Pythagorean Theorem to determine side lengths. In this lesson, you will explore the diagonals of various shapes.

1. Rectangle *ABCD* is shown.

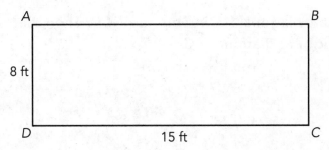

a. Draw diagonal *AC* in Rectangle *ABCD*. Then, determine the length of diagonal *AC*.

Be on the lookout for right triangles.

b. Draw diagonal *BD* in Rectangle *ABCD*. Then, determine the length of diagonal *BD*.

c. What can you conclude about the diagonals of this rectangle?

2. Square *ABCD* is shown.

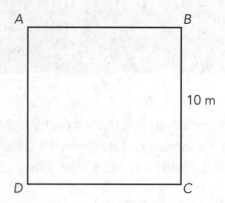

a. Draw diagonal *AC* in Square *ABCD*. Then, determine the length of diagonal *AC*.

b. Draw diagonal *BD* in Square *ABCD*. Then, determine the length of diagonal *BD*.

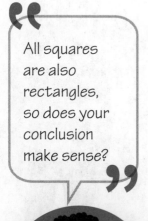

All squares are also rectangles, so does your conclusion make sense?

c. What can you conclude about the diagonals of this square?

3. Graph and label the coordinates of the vertices of
   Trapezoid ABCD: A (1, 2), B (7, 2), C (7, 5), D (3, 5).

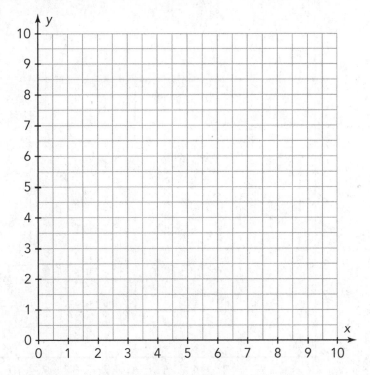

a. Draw diagonal AC in Trapezoid ABCD.

b. What right triangle can be used to determine the length of
   diagonal AC?

c. Determine the length of diagonal AC.

d. Draw diagonal BD in Trapezoid ABCD.

e. What right triangle can be used to determine the length of
   diagonal BD?

f. Determine the length of diagonal BD.

g. What can you conclude about the diagonals of this trapezoid?

4. **Graph and label the coordinates of the vertices of isosceles Trapezoid *ABCD*: *A* (1, 2), *B* (9, 2), *C* (7, 5), *D* (3, 5).**

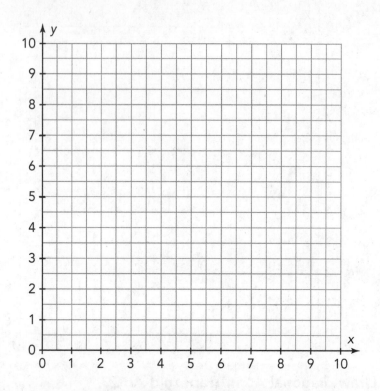

How is this trapezoid different from the first trapezoid you drew?

a. **Draw diagonal *AC* in Trapezoid *ABCD*.**

b. **What right triangle can be used to determine the length of diagonal *AC*?**

c.   Determine the length of diagonal AC.

What is your prediction about the diagonals of this isosceles trapezoid

d.   Draw diagonal *BD* in Trapezoid *ABCD*.

e.   What right triangle can be used to determine the length of diagonal *BD*?

f.   Determine the length of diagonal *BD*.

g.   What can you conclude about the diagonals of this isosceles trapezoid?

Use your knowledge of right triangles, the Pythagorean Theorem, and area formulas.

1. Determine the area of each shaded region. Use 3.14 for π and round to the nearest tenth.
   a. A rectangle is inscribed in a circle as shown.

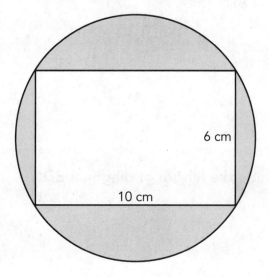

6 cm

10 cm

   b. The figure is composed of a right triangle and a semi-circle.

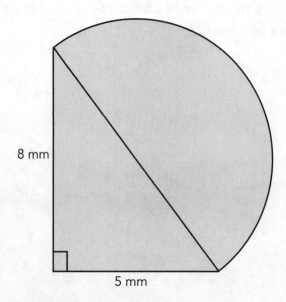

8 mm

5 mm

Diagonals in Solid Figures

A rectangular box of long-stem roses is 18 inches in length, 6 inches in width, and 4 inches in height.

Without bending a long-stem rose, you are to determine the maximum length of a rose that will fit into the box.

1. What makes this problem different from all of the previous applications of the Pythagorean Theorem?

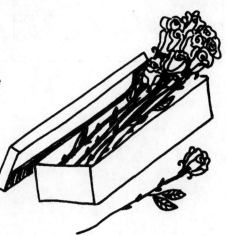

2. Compare a two-dimensional diagonal to a three-dimensional diagonal. Describe the similarities and differences.

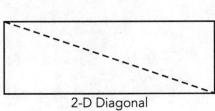

2-D Diagonal

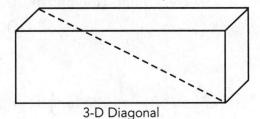

3-D Diagonal

3. Which diagonal represents the maximum length of a rose that can fit into a box?

4. Consider the rectangular solid shown.

   a. Draw all of the sides in the rectangular solid you cannot see using dotted lines.

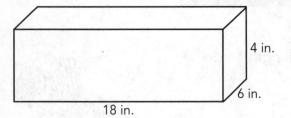

4 in.

6 in.

18 in.

   b. Draw a three-dimensional diagonal in the rectangular solid.

   c. Let's consider that the three-dimensional diagonal you drew in the rectangular solid is also the hypotenuse of a right triangle. If a vertical edge is one of the legs of that right triangle, where is the second leg of that same right triangle?

   d. Draw the second leg using a dotted line. Then lightly shade the right triangle.

   e. Determine the length of the second leg you drew.

   f. Determine the length of the three-dimensional diagonal.

   g. What does the length of the three-dimensional diagonal represent in terms of this problem situation?

5. Describe how the Pythagorean Theorem was used to solve this problem.

Practice with Three-Dimensional Diagonals

Determine the length of the diagonal of each rectangular solid.

1.

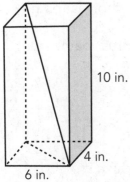

10 in.

4 in.

6 in.

2.

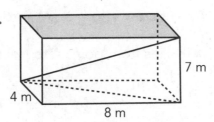

7 m

4 m

8 m

3.

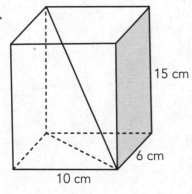

15 cm

6 cm

10 cm

4.

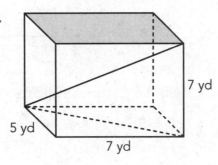

7 yd

5 yd

7 yd

5.

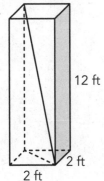

12 ft

2 ft

2 ft

6.

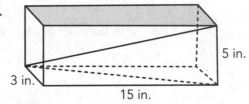

5 in.

3 in.

15 in.

TALK the TALK

The Ant and the Fly Again

A rectangular room is 10 ft × 16 ft × 8 ft.

An ant crawls from point *A* to point *B* taking the shortest path.

A fly flies from point *A* to point *B* taking the shortest path.

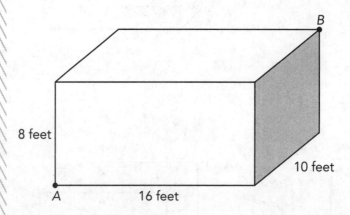

1. Whose path was shorter?

2. How much shorter is the shorter path?

Assignment

Write

In your own words, explain how you can determine a diagonal length inside a rectangular prism. Use an example to illustrate your explanation.

Remember

You can use the Pythagorean Theorem to determine the length of a diagonal in a two- or three-dimensional figure.

Practice

1. Determine the length of the diagonals in each given quadrilateral.

   a. The figure is a square with side lengths of 15 feet.

   b. The figure is a rectangle with a length of 18 inches and a height of 10 inches.

   c.

   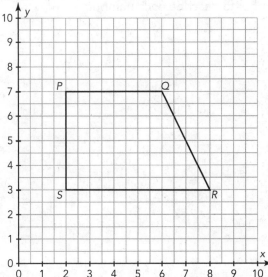

   d.

   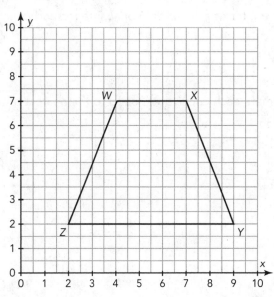

2. A packing company is in the planning stages of creating a box that includes a three-dimensional diagonal support inside the box. The box has a width of 5 feet, a length of 6 feet, and a height of 8 feet. How long will the diagonal support need to be?

3. A plumber needs to transport a 12-foot pipe to a jobsite. The interior of his van is 90 inches in length, 40 inches in width, and 40 inches in height. Will the pipe fit inside his van?

4. George is landscaping the flower beds in his front yard. He chooses to plant a tree that measures 5 feet from the root ball to the top. The interior of his car is 60 inches in length, 45 inches in width, and 40 inches in height. Will the tree fit inside George's car?

Stretch

Norton thought he knew a shortcut to determine the length of a three-dimensional diagonal. He said, "All you have to do is calculate the sum of the squares of the rectangular solid's three perpendicular edges (the length, the width, and the height), and that sum would be equivalent to the square of the three-dimensional diagonal." Does this work? Explain your reasoning.

Review

Determine the distance between each pair of points.

1. $(-9, -5)$, $(3, 12)$
2. $(5, 5)$, $(1, -10)$

Use the terms *rational, irrational, integer,* and *counting number* to describe each number.

3. $-\sqrt{100}$
4. $\frac{75}{4}$

Estimate each cube root. Round to the nearest tenth.

5. $\sqrt[3]{36}$
6. $\sqrt[3]{75}$

Pythagorean Theorem Summary

KEY TERMS

- hypotenuse
- legs
- Pythagorean Theorem
- proof
- diagonal of a square

- converse
- Converse of the Pythagorean Theorem
- Pythagorean triple
- diagonal

LESSON 1

The Right Triangle Connection

In the right triangle shown, the lengths of the sides are a, b, and c.

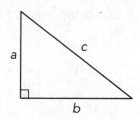

The side opposite the right angle is called the **hypotenuse**. The other two sides are called **legs** of the right triangle. In the figure, the sides with lengths a and b are the legs, and the side with length c is the hypotenuse.

The special relationship that exists among the squares of the lengths of the sides of a right triangle is known as the Pythagorean Theorem. The **Pythagorean Theorem** states that the sum of the squares of the lengths of the legs of a right triangle equals the square of the length of the hypotenuse: $a^2 + b^2 = c^2$.

There are different ways to prove that the Pythagorean Theorem holds true for all right triangles. A **proof** is a line of reasoning used to validate a theorem. In some proofs, you need to draw the diagonal of a square. A **diagonal of a square** is a line segment connecting opposite vertices of the square.

The Pythagorean Theorem can be used to determine unknown side lengths in a right triangle if you know two of the other side lengths.

For example, suppose you want to determine the length of the hypotenuse of the right triangle with leg lengths of 2 and 4.

$$c^2 = 2^2 + 4^2$$
$$c^2 = 4 + 16 = 20$$
$$c = \sqrt{20} \approx 4.5$$

The length of the hypotenuse is approximately 4.5 units.

The **converse** of a theorem is created when the if-then parts of that theorem are exchanged. The **Converse of the Pythagorean Theorem** states that if the sum of the squares of the two shorter sides of a triangle equals the square of the longest side, then the triangle is a right triangle.

Consider a triangle with the side lengths 9, 12, and 15.

$$9^2 + 12^2 \stackrel{?}{=} 15^2$$
$$81 + 144 \stackrel{?}{=} 225$$
$$225 = 225$$

This is a right triangle according to the Converse of the Pythagorean Theorem.

Any set of three positive integers a, b, and c that satisfies the equation $a^2 + b^2 = c^2$ is a **Pythagorean triple**. The integers 3, 4, and 5 form a Pythagorean triple because $3^2 + 4^2 = 5^2$. Given a Pythagorean triple, you can identify other right triangles by multiplying each side length by the same factor.

Pythagoras Meets Descartes

You can calculate the distance between two points on the coordinate plane by drawing a right triangle. When you think about this line segment as the hypotenuse of the right triangle, you can use the Pythagorean Theorem.

For example, consider the points $(-5, 2)$ and $(-8, 8)$. You can calculate the distance between these two points by first determining the length of each leg of a right triangle formed using that line segment as the hypotenuse. One leg measures 3 units, and the other leg measures 6 units.

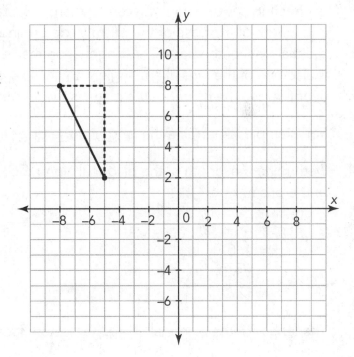

$$3^2 + 6^2 = c^2$$
$$9 + 36 = c^2$$
$$45 = c^2$$
$$c = \sqrt{45}$$

The distance between points $(-5, 2)$ and $(-8, 8)$ is $\sqrt{45}$ units.

The distance between two points on a coordinate plane is always a positive number.

You can use the Pythagorean Theorem to determine the length of a diagonal in a two- or three-dimensional figure.

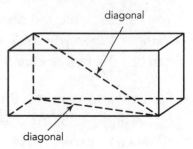

diagonal

diagonal

In a three-dimensional figure, a **diagonal** is a line segment connecting any two non-adjacent vertices. You can use the width and length of the base of the prism to determine the measure of the diagonal of the base. The diagonal on the base of the prism is also one of the legs of a triangle with an inner-diagonal as the hypotenuse. The height of the prism is the length of the other leg.

For example, determine the length of the diagonal of the rectangular prism shown.

Determine the length of the diagonal along the bottom face of the prism.

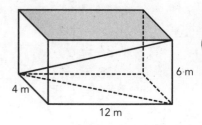

6 m

4 m

12 m

$$c^2 = 4^2 + 12^2$$
$$c^2 = 160$$
$$\sqrt{c^2} = \sqrt{160}$$
$$c \approx 12.6$$

The length of the diagonal along the bottom face is approximately 12.6 m.

Determine the length of the 3-D diagonal.

$$c^2 = 6^2 + 12.6^2$$
$$c^2 = 194.76$$
$$\sqrt{c^2} = \sqrt{194.76}$$
$$c \approx 13.96$$

The length of the 3-D diagonal is approximately 13.96 m.

MODULE 5

APPLYING POWERS

The lessons in this module build on your knowledge of exponents to develop new rules for operating with integer exponents. You will learn how to write, recognize, compare, and operate with numbers expressed in scientific notation. You will build on your prior experiences with the volume of prisms and pyramids to develop formulas for the volume of cylinders, cones, and spheres.

Exponents and Scientific Notation

The Pinwheel Galaxy, also known as Messier 101, is a spiral galaxy that is 21 million light-years away from earth in the constellation Ursa Major. For huge distances and tiny distances, you'll want to use scientific notation.

Module 5: Applying Powers

TOPIC 1: EXPONENTS AND SCIENTIFIC NOTATION

In this topic, students learn and apply properties of integer exponents. Students then explore a specific application of exponents and the exponent rules: scientific notation. They learn to express numbers in standard form in scientific notation and those in scientific notation in standard form. Throughout the conversion activities, students attend to the reasonableness of their answers. Once students understand scientific notation, they multiply, divide, add, and subtract numbers expressed in scientific notation, making connections to the exponent rules learned earlier in the topic.

Where have we been?

Students have been working with exponents since grade 5. They have learned to write and evaluate numerical and algebraic expressions with whole number exponents. In this topic, students expand on that knowledge.

Where are we going?

In high school, students will evaluate rational number exponents. Therefore, this topic provides a bridge between students' first formal use of exponents and a more rigorous and abstract exposure in high school. Scientific notation, an application of exponents, will arise in students' science courses in middle school and high school, particularly in the study of chemistry.

Using Tree Diagrams to Study Exponential Growth

A tree diagram can show exponential growth. This tree diagram is actually a family tree—for a dog. Rickson represents 2^0, or 1, dog. His parents in Generation 1 are 2^1, or 2, dogs. Generation 2 has 2^2, or 4, dogs, and Generation 3 shows 2^3, or 8, dogs.

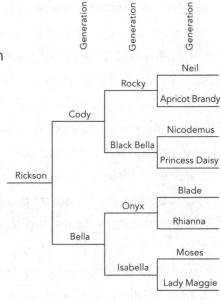

Myth: Faster = smarter.

In most cases, speed has nothing to do with how smart you are. Why is that? Because it largely depends on how familiar you are with a topic. For example, a bike mechanic can look at a bike for about 8 seconds and tell you details about the bike that you probably didn't even notice (e.g., the front tire is on backwards). Is that person smart? Sure! Suppose, instead, you show the same bike mechanic a car. Will they be able to recall the same amount of detail as for the bike? No!

It's easy to confuse speed with understanding. Speed is associated with the memorization of facts. Understanding, on the other hand, is a methodical, time-consuming process. Understanding is the result of asking lots of questions and seeing connections between different ideas. Many mathematicians who won the Fields Medal (i.e., the Nobel prize for mathematics) describe themselves as extremely slow thinkers. That's because mathematical thinking requires understanding over memorization.

#mathmythbusted

Talking Points

You can support your student's learning by approaching problems slowly. Students may observe a classmate learning things very quickly, and they can easily come to believe that mathematics is about getting the right answer as quickly as possible. When this doesn't happen for them, future encounters with math can raise anxiety, making problem solving more difficult, and reinforcing a student's view of himself or herself as "not good at math." Slowing down is not the ultimate cure for math difficulties. But it's a good first step for children who are struggling. You can reinforce the view that learning with understanding takes time, and that slow, deliberate work is the rule, not the exception.

Key Terms

base
The base of a power is the factor that is multiplied repeatedly in the power.

exponent
The exponent of a power is the number of times the base is used as a factor.

scientific notation
In general terms, $a \times 10^n$ is a number written in scientific notation, where a is greater than or equal to 1 and less than 10, and n is any integer. The number a is called the mantissa, and n is the called the characteristic.

It's a Generational Thing

Properties of Powers with Integer Exponents

1

WARM UP

Simplify each expression.

1. $(-10)(-10)(-10)$

2. $(-10)(-10)(-10)(-10)$

3. $(-1)(2)(-3)(4)(-5)$

4. $(-2)(-3)(-4)(-5)$

LEARNING GOALS

- Expand a power into a product.
- Write a product as a power.
- Simplify numeric expressions containing integer exponents.
- Develop rules to simplify a product of powers, a power of a power, and a quotient of powers.
- Apply the properties of integer exponents to create equivalent expressions.

KEY TERMS

- power
- base
- exponent

You have learned how to evaluate numeric expressions involving whole-number exponents. In this lesson, you will develop the properties of integer exponents to generate equivalent numeric expressions.

Three Generations

Jake adopted an English Mastiff puppy that he named Rickson. The breeder provided documentation that verified Rickson's lineage for three generations, as shown.

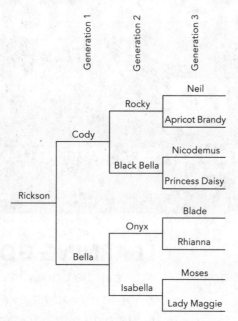

A dog's lineage is similar to a person's family tree. It shows a dog's parents, grandparents, and great-grandparents.

1. **How many parents does Rickson have? What are his parents' names?**

2. **How many grandparents does Rickson have?**

3. **How many great-grandparents does Rickson have?**

4. **What pattern is there in the number of dogs in each generation?**

<table>
<tr><td>ACTIVITY
1.1</td><td>Review of Powers and
Exponents</td><td></td></tr>
</table>

Jake wants to trace Rickson's lineage back seven generations. How many sires (male parents) and dams (female parents) are there in seven generations of Rickson's lineage?

1. Complete the second column of the table, Number of Sires and Dams, to show the total number of dogs in each generation.

	Number of Sires and Dams		
Generation 1			
Generation 2			
Generation 3			
Generation 4			
Generation 5			
Generation 6			
Generation 7			

An expression used to represent the product of a repeated multiplication is a *power*. A **power** has a *base* and an *exponent*. The **base** of a power is the expression that is used as a factor in the repeated multiplication. The **exponent** of a power is the number of times that the base is used as a factor in the repeated multiplication.

WORKED EXAMPLE

You can write a power as a product by writing out the repeated multiplication.

$$2^7 = (2)(2)(2)(2)(2)(2)(2)$$

The power 2^7 can be read as:
- "two to the seventh power."
- "the seventh power of two."
- "two raised to the seventh power."

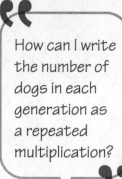

How can I write the number of dogs in each generation as a repeated multiplication?

2. Label the third column Expanded Notation. Then write each generation total as a product.

3. Label the fourth column of the table Power. Then write each generation total as a power.

4. How many dogs are in Rickson's lineage in the 12th generation back? Write your answer as a power, and then use a calculator to determine the total number of dogs.

5. How many total sires and dams are there in all three generations shown in Rickson's lineage? Explain your calculation.

In this activity, you will investigate the role of parentheses in expressions containing exponents.

1. **Identify the base(s) and exponent(s) in each. Then, write each power as a product. Finally, evaluate the power.**

   a. 5^3

   b. $(-9)^5$

   c. -11^3

   d. $(4)^5(3)^6$

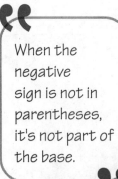

2. **Write each as a product. Then, calculate the product.**

   a. -1^2 b. -1^3 c. -1^4 d. -1^5

   e. $(-1)^2$ f. $(-1)^3$ g. $(-1)^4$ h. $(-1)^5$

> When the negative sign is not in parentheses, it's not part of the base.

3. **What conclusion can you draw about a negative number raised to an odd power?**

4. **What conclusion can you draw about a negative number raised to an even power?**

File sizes of eBooks, podcasts, and song downloads depend on the complexity of the content and the number of images.

1 gigabyte = 1024 megabytes

1 megabyte = 1024 kilobytes

1 kilobyte = 1024 bytes

WORKED EXAMPLE

Suppose that a medium-sized eBook contains about 1 megabyte (MB) of information.

Since 1 megabyte is 1024 kilobytes (kB), and 1 kilobyte is 1024 bytes (B), you can multiply to determine the number of bytes in the eBook:

$$1 \text{ MB} = (1024 \text{ kB}) \left(\frac{1024 \text{ B}}{1 \text{ kB}} \right) = 1{,}048{,}576 \text{ B}$$

There are 1,048,576 bytes in the eBook.

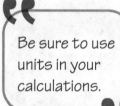

Be sure to use units in your calculations.

1. One model of an eBook can store up to 256 MB of data. A USB jump drive can hold 2 GB of storage. Use the method shown in the worked example to calculate each.

   a. Calculate the number of bytes the eBook can store.

      256 MB × _____ × _____

   b. A USB jump drive can hold 2 GB of storage. How many bytes can the USB jump drive hold?

      2 GB × _____ × _____ × _____

   c. How many times more storage space does the jump drive have than the eBook? Show your work.

      $$\frac{2 \times \rule{2cm}{0.15mm} \times \rule{2cm}{0.15mm} \times}{256 \times \rule{2cm}{0.15mm} \times}$$

WORKED EXAMPLE

Computers use binary math, or the base-2 system, instead of the base-10 system.

<u>Base 10</u>

$10^1 = 10$

$10^2 = (10)(10) = 100$

$10^3 = (10)(10)(10) = 1000$

<u>Base 2</u>

$2^1 = 2$

$2^2 = (2)(2) = 4$

$2^3 = (2)(2)(2) = 8$

2. Revisit Question 1, parts (a) through (c), by rewriting each factor and either your product or quotient as a power of 2.

   a.

   b.

   c.

3. Analyze your answers to Question 2. What do you notice about all the bases in Question 2?

4. In parts (a) and (b), how does the exponent in each product relate to the exponents in the factors?

5. In part (c), how does the exponent in the quotient relate to the exponents in the numerator and denominator?

ACTIVITY 1.4 | Product of Powers

In this activity, you will explore different expressions to develop rules to evaluate powers.

1. Rewrite each expression as a product using expanded notation. Then identify the base or bases and record the number of times the base is used as a factor.

   a. $2^4 \cdot 2^3$

   b. $(-3)^3(-3)^3$

   c. $(4)(4^5)$

   d. $(5^2)(6^2)(5^3)(6)$

   e. $(9^3)(4^2)(9^2)(4^5)$

2. Rewrite each of your answers from Question 1 as a power or a product of powers.

3. What relationship do you notice between the exponents in the original expression and the number of factors?

4. Write a rule that you can use to multiply powers.

A power can also be raised to a power.

WORKED EXAMPLE

The exponential expression $(4^2)^3$ is a power to a power. It can be written as two repeated multiplication expressions using the definition of a power.

$$(4^2)^3 = (4^2)(4^2)(4^2)$$

$$= (4)(4)(4)(4)(4)(4)$$

There are 6 factors of 4.

5. Use the definition of a power to write repeated multiplication expressions for each power to a power, as modeled in the worked example. Then, record the number of factors.

   a. $(8^2)^3$ b. $(5^4)^2$

   c. $-(6^1)^6$ d. $((-6)^2)^2$

6. What relationship do you notice between the exponents in each expression in Question 5 and the number of factors? Write each expression as a single power.

7. Write a rule that you can use to raise a power to a power.

8. Simplify each expression using the rules that you wrote.

a. $6^4 \cdot 6^3$

b. $9^7 \cdot 9^8$

c. $(4^3)^5$

d. $(2)(3)(8)^5$

e. $5^5 \cdot 5^2 \cdot 5$

f. $((2)(3))^4$

9. Ramon says that $2^6 = 12$. Randy says that $2^6 = 64$. Who is correct? Explain your reasoning.

10. Isabel says that $2^2 + 2^3 = 2^5$, and Elizabeth says that $2^2 + 2^3 \neq 2^5$. Who is correct? Explain your reasoning.

Now, let's investigate what happens when you divide powers with like bases.

1. Write each numerator and denominator as a product. Then, simplify each expression and write the simplified expression using exponents.

   a. $\dfrac{9^5}{9^2}$ b. $\dfrac{5^6}{5^3}$ c. $\dfrac{10^8}{10^6}$ d. $\dfrac{10^2}{10}$

2. What relationship do you notice between the exponents in the numerator and denominator and the exponents in the simplified expression?

3. Write a rule that you can use to divide with powers.

4. Simplify each expression using the rule that you wrote for a quotient of powers.

   a. $\dfrac{6^8}{6^3}$ b. $-\dfrac{9^7}{9^5}$ c. $\dfrac{2^3}{3^2}$

You know that any number divided by itself is 1. How can you use that knowledge to develop another rule to evaluate powers?

Consider each representation of 1.

$$\frac{4}{4} = 1 \qquad\qquad \frac{9}{9} = 1 \qquad\qquad \frac{25}{25} = 1$$

1. **Rewrite the numerator and denominator of each fraction as a power. Do not simplify.**

2. **Next, simplify the fractions you just wrote using the Quotient Rule of Powers. Leave your answer as a power. What do you notice?**

An exception is that 0^0 is not equal to 1, because that would mean that using zero as a factor zero times would give you 1, and that's not possible.

3. **Write a rule that you can use when raising any base to the zero power.**

Let's determine how to use powers to represent numbers that are less than 1.

You know that you can use powers to represent numbers that are greater than or equal to 1.

4. Let's start with 1 and multiply by 10 three times.

   a. Complete the representation. Write each as a power.

   $$1 \quad = \quad 10^0$$

   Multiply by 10 = _____ = _____

   Multiply by 10 = _____ = _____

   Multiply by 10 = _____ = _____

   b. Describe what happens to the exponents as the number becomes greater.

5. Now, let's start with 1 and divide by 10 three times.

   a. Complete the representation. Write the division as a fraction, and then rewrite using the definition of powers. Next, apply the Quotient Rule of Powers, and finally, simplify each expression.

   $$1 \quad = \quad \frac{10^0}{10^0} \quad = \quad 10^{0-0} \quad = \quad 10^0$$

   Divide by 10 = $\frac{1}{10}$ = $\frac{10^0}{10^1}$ = 10^{0-1} = 10^{-1}

   Divide by 10 = ____ = ____ = ____ = ____

   Divide by 10 = ____ = ____ = ____ = ____

   b. Describe what happens to the exponents as the number becomes less.

   c. Write each of the powers as a decimal.

LESSON 1: It's a Generational Thing • M5-19

6. Rewrite each sequence of numbers using the definition of powers.

   a. $\frac{1}{8}, \frac{1}{4}, \frac{1}{2}, 1, 2, 4, 8$

   b. $\frac{1}{27}, \frac{1}{9}, \frac{1}{3}, 1, 3, 9, 27$

   c. Describe the exponents in the sequence.

7. Simplify each expression using the Quotient Rule of Powers. Then, write each as a decimal.

   a. $\frac{10^0}{10^3}$

   b. $\frac{10^0}{10^5}$

   c. $\frac{10^0}{10^4}$

8. Complete the table shown.

Unit	Number of Grams	Number of Grams as an Expression with a Positive Exponent	Number of Grams as an Expression with a Negative Exponent
Milligram	$\frac{1}{1000}$		10^{-3}
Microgram		$\frac{1}{10^6}$	
Nanogram	$\frac{1}{1,000,000,000}$		10^{-9}
Picogram		$\frac{1}{10^{12}}$	

9. Rewrite the power so that the exponent is positive.

   a. 8^{-4}

   b. 5^{-6}

   c. 7^{-5}

   d. $(4^{-2})(3^{-3})$

10. Complete the table shown.

Given Expression	Expression with a Positive Exponent	Value of Expression
$\dfrac{1}{3^{-2}}$		
$\dfrac{1}{4^{-2}}$		
$\dfrac{1}{5^{-2}}$		
$\dfrac{2^{-2}}{1}$	$\dfrac{1}{2^2}$	$\dfrac{1}{4}$
$\dfrac{3^{-2}}{1}$		
$\dfrac{5^{-2}}{1}$		

11. Describe how to rewrite any expression with a negative exponent in the numerator.

12. Describe how to rewrite any expression with a negative exponent in the denominator.

TALK the TALK

Simplifying

In this lesson, you have developed rules for operating with powers. A summary of these rules is shown in the table.

Properties of Powers	Words	Rule
Product Rule of Powers	To multiply powers with the same base, keep the base and add the exponents.	$a^m \cdot a^n = a^{m+n}$
Power to a Power Rule	To simplify a power to a power, keep the base and multiply the exponents.	$(a^m)^n = a^{mn}$
Quotient Rule of Powers	To divide powers with the same base, keep the base and subtract the exponents.	$\frac{a^m}{a^n} = a^{m-n}$, if $a \neq 0$
Zero Power	The zero power of any number expect for 0 is 1.	$a^0 = 1$, if $a \neq 0$
Negative Exponents in the Numerator	An expression with a negative exponent in the numerator and a 1 in the denominator equals 1 divided by the power with its opposite exponent placed in the denominator.	$a^{-m} = \frac{1}{a^m}$, if $a \neq 0$ and $m > 0$
Negative Exponents in the Denominator	An expression with a negative exponent in the denominator and a 1 in the numerator equals the power with its opposite exponent.	$\frac{1}{a^{-m}} = a^m$, if $a \neq 0$ and $m > 0$

Simplify each expression using the properties of powers.

1. $2a^8 \cdot 2a^6$

2. $4b^2 \cdot 8b^9$

3. $-3c \cdot 5c^3 \cdot 2c^9$

4. $(3d^2)^3$

5. $(10ef^3)^5$

6. $\dfrac{f^8}{f^3}$

7. $\dfrac{10g^4}{5g^6}$

8. $\dfrac{30h^8}{15h^2}$

9. $\dfrac{35i^7j^3}{7i^2j^3}$

10. $\left(\dfrac{a^2}{a^5}\right)^0$

11. $\dfrac{2^2}{2^6}$

12. $(4x^2)(3x^5)$

13. $(9^4)(9^{-5})$

14. $(8^0)(8^{-2})$

15. $\dfrac{3^{-3}}{3^{-3}}$

16. $\dfrac{4^{-2}}{4^{-3}}$

17. $\dfrac{(-3)^2}{(-3)^4}$

18. $\dfrac{h^3}{h^5}$

19. $\dfrac{x^4}{x^5}$

20. $\dfrac{m^2 p^{-2}}{m^4 p^3}$

Assignment

Write

Use the term *base*, *power*, or *exponent* to complete each sentence.

1. The _____ of a power is the number of times that the factor is repeatedly multiplied.

2. An expression used to represent a factor as repeated multiplication is called a _____.

3. The _____ of a power is the repeated factor in a power.

Remember

Properties of Powers	Words	Rule
Product Rule of Powers	To multiply powers with the same base, keep the base and add the exponents.	$a^m \cdot a^n = a^{m+n}$
Power to a Power Rule	To simplify a power to a power, keep the base and multiply the exponents.	$(a^m)^n = a^{mn}$
Quotient Rule of Powers	To divide powers with the same base, keep the base and subtract the exponents.	$\dfrac{a^m}{a^n} = a^{m-n}$, if $a \neq 0$

Practice

1. As the principal of Hope Middle School, Mr. Williams is in charge of notifying his staff about school delays or cancellations due to weather, power outages, or other unexpected events. Mr. Williams starts a phone chain by calling three staff members. Each of these staff members then calls three more staff members, who each call three more staff members. This process completes the calling list.

   a. Excluding Mr. Williams, how many staff members are there at Hope Middle School? Explain your calculation.

   b. Complete the first three columns in the table.

	Round 1	Round 2	Round 3	Round 4
Number of calls made				
Expanded notation				
Power				

   c. Dr. Novella, superintendent of the school district, decides that she should start the phone chain instead of the school principals. She starts the calling list by calling each of the principals of the three schools in her district. The principals continue the phone chain as described previously. Explain why the table in part (b) can be used to represent Dr. Novella's phone chain.

   d. Complete the fourth column in the table to represent the fourth round of calls in Dr. Novella's phone chain.

   e. How many calls are made in the fourth round? Show your work.

   f. Excluding Dr. Novella, how many principals and staff members are there in the entire school district? Explain your calculation.

2. The *hertz* (Hz) is a unit of frequency that represents the number of complete cycles per second. is used to measure repeating events, both scientific and general. For instance, a clock ticks at 1 Hz. One scientific application is the electromagnetic spectrum, or the range of all possible frequencies of electromagnetic waves. The spectrum includes frequencies from everyday contexts, such as radio and TV signals, microwaves, light (infrared, visible, and ultraviolet), and X-rays.

Name	Frequency
1 kilohertz (kHz)	1000 Hz
1 megahertz (MHz)	1000 kHz
1 gigahertz (GHz)	1000 MHz
1 terahertz (THz)	1000 GHz

For each question, use powers to write a mathematical expression. Then evaluate each expression. Express your answer as a power.

a. How many hertz are in 1 gigahertz? 1 terahertz?

b. A television channel has a frequency of 60 megahertz. What is the channel's frequency in hertz?

c. The frequency of a microwave is 30 gigahertz. What is the microwave's frequency in hertz?

d. The frequency of a visible ray of light is 1000 terahertz. A radio station has a frequency of 100 megahertz. How many times greater is the frequency of the light than the frequency of the radio station?

3. Each expression has been simplified incorrectly. Explain the mistake that occurred, and then make the correction.

a. $(-2x)^3 = 8x^3$

b. $\frac{16x^5}{4x} = 12x^4$

c. $(x^2y^4)^3 = x^6y^7$.

d. $(x^5y^7)(x^2yz) = x^7y^7z$

4. When you take a picture, the camera shutter controls how much light reaches the film or the digital image sensor. The shutter speed is the amount of time, in seconds, that the shutter stays open. Write each shutter speed as a power with a negative exponent.

a. $\frac{1}{4}$ second

b. $\frac{1}{8}$ second

c. $\frac{1}{125}$ second

d. $\frac{1}{1000}$ second

5. True or False: A number raised to a negative power is always a negative number. Give an example to support your answer.

6. Give an example of a number raised to a negative exponent that is a negative number.

7. Simplify each expression using the properties of powers. Show your work.

a. $\frac{10^2}{10^5}$

b. $\frac{3^{-5}}{3^{-5}}$

c. $(6x^4)(2x^{-2})$

d. $(7^{-6})(7^4)$

e. $(4^0)(4^{-3})$

f. $\frac{5^2}{5^{-2}}$

g. $\frac{4^{-1}}{4^2}$

h. $\frac{p^4}{p^9}$

i. $\frac{m^{-2}}{m^{-6}}$

j. $\frac{q^{-2}r^3}{q^6r^{-4}}$

Stretch

Exponents can be stacked as high as you like. Some mathematicians have used double arrows to represent repeated exponents. For example, $3 \uparrow \uparrow 3$ represents $3^{3^{3}}$, or 3^{27}.

Write different numbers using double-arrow notation. How can you write 10 billion using this notation?

Review

Use the Pythagorean Theorem and its converse to answer each question.

1. You are making a picture frame in the craft cabin. The frame measures 9 inches by 12 inches. You measure the diagonal and it is 17 inches. Is the frame rectangular?

2. On the third day at camp, you go canoeing on the camp lake. You paddle from the dock due north for 500 yards and then due west for 475 yards. How far are you from the dock? Round your answer to the nearest whole number.

3. Complete the table of Pythagorean Triples.

Leg 1	Leg 2	Hypotenuse
3 feet	4 feet	
6 feet	8 feet	
9 feet	12 feet	
12 feet	16 feet	
15 feet	20 feet	

4. Use what you know about approximating square roots to answer each question.
   a. Explain how you know that the value of $\sqrt{12}$ is between 3 and 4.
   b. Shade between two values to show where $\sqrt{12}$ lies on the number line.

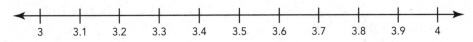

Show What You Know

2

Analyzing Properties of Powers

Warm Up

Simplify each expression.

1. $\frac{1}{3^2}$

2. $-(2^5)^2$

3. $\frac{2}{5} \cdot 10$

4. $\frac{32 + 8}{80 \div 2}$

LEARNING GOALS

- Review the Product Rule of Powers.
- Review the Power to a Power Property.
- Review the Quotient Rule of Powers Property.
- Generate equivalent expressions by applying properties of integer exponents.

You have learned about the properties of powers with integer exponents. How can you use these properties to justify your reasoning when solving problems?

Are They Equal?

The symbol for "is equal to" is =. The symbol for "is not equal to" is ≠. Write the appropriate symbol in each box to compare the two expressions. Explain your reasoning.

1. 2^3 $\boxed{}$ 2^{-3}

2. $\dfrac{1}{2^3}$ $\boxed{}$ 2^{-3}

3. $\dfrac{1}{2^{-3}}$ $\boxed{}$ 2^3

4. $\dfrac{1}{2^{-3}}$ $\boxed{}$ 2^{-3}

Analyze the worked example.

WORKED EXAMPLE

$\left(\dfrac{2^5}{2^4}\right)^3 =$

$= (2^1)^3$ Quotient Rule of Powers

$= 2^3$ Power to a Power Rule

1. **Identify the rule that justifies each step to simplify the expression.**

a. $2^4 \cdot (-4^1)^3$

$= 2^4 \cdot (-4^3)$ _____

$= (16)(-64)$ _____

b. $\dfrac{(3 \cdot 5^3)^2}{(2 \cdot 5^4)^2}$

$= \dfrac{(3^2 \cdot 5^6)}{(2^2 \cdot 5^8)}$ _____

$= \dfrac{3^2}{(2^2 \cdot 5^2)}$ _____

$= \dfrac{9}{4 \cdot 25}$ _____

$= \dfrac{9}{100}$ _____

2. Simplify each expression using the properties of powers. Express your answers using only positive exponents.

a. $\dfrac{2(6)^3(4)^5}{4(6)^3(4)^2}$

b. $\dfrac{(4(1)^2(3)^3)^4}{(2(1)^3(3)^2)^3}$

c. $\dfrac{(-3(5)^2(8)^4)^8}{(-3(5)^2(8)^4)^8}$

d. $\dfrac{(10^5 \cdot 10^5)}{10^6}$

Analyzing Errors in Applying Properties of Powers

Determine which student(s) used the properties of powers correctly. Explain why the other expressions are not correct.

1. $\dfrac{5^7 4^4}{5^3 4^9}$

   Adam wrote $5^{10} 4^{13}$.

   Nic wrote $\dfrac{5^4}{4^5}$.

   Shane wrote $5^4 4^5$.

   Who is correct?

2. $\dfrac{2(3)^{-4}}{5^{-2}}$

   Adam wrote $\dfrac{2(5)^2}{3^4}$.

   Nic wrote $\dfrac{5^2}{2(3)^4}$.

   Shane wrote $\dfrac{2(3)^4}{5^2}$.

   Who is correct?

3. Each expression has been simplified incorrectly. Explain the mistake that occurred, and then make the correction.

   a. $(-2 \cdot 7)^3 = 8 \cdot 7^3$

   b. $\dfrac{16 \cdot 7^5}{4 \cdot 7} = 12 \cdot 7^4$

   c. $(7^2 10^4)^3 = 7^6 10^7$

   d. $(7^5 10^7)(7^2 10 \cdot 2) = 7^7 10^7 2$

TALK the TALK

Organize the Properties

1. Create graphic organizers for each.

   Product Rule of Powers

   Quotient Rule of Powers

   Power of a Power Rule

   Zero Power Rule

   Negative Exponent Rule

As you are creating your representations, consider the following:

Definition in your own words: How would you describe this property to a friend?

Facts/Characteristics: Are there specific characteristics if the numbers are positive or negative? Does this property work the same for variables and numbers?

Examples: Include examples with variables and different types of numbers (e.g., positive, negative, and fractions).

General Rule: Use variables. Be mindful of when a variable cannot be zero.

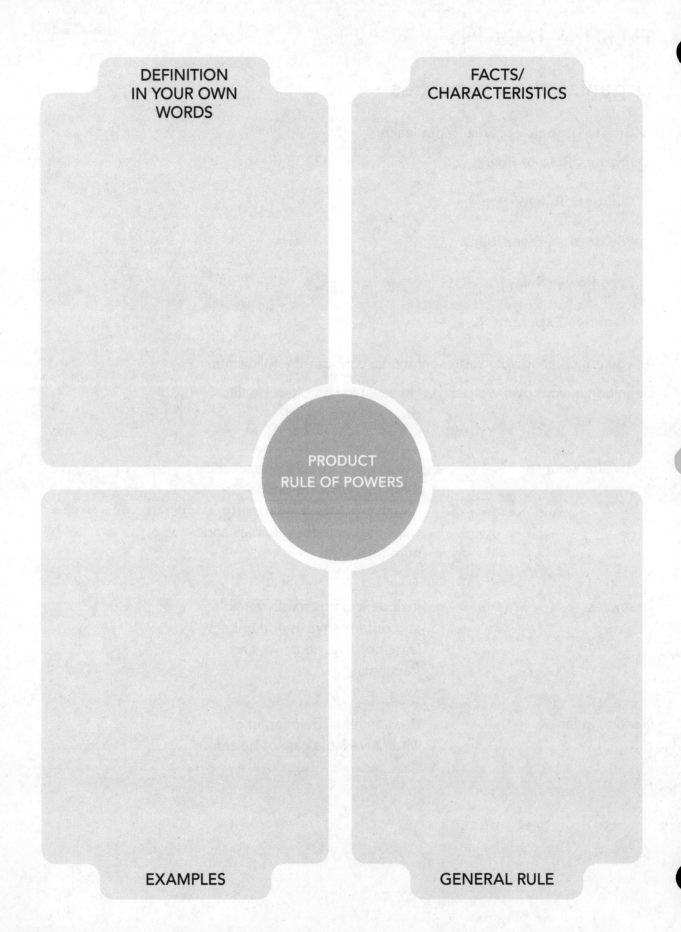

DEFINITION
IN YOUR OWN
WORDS

FACTS/
CHARACTERISTICS

PRODUCT
RULE OF POWERS

EXAMPLES

GENERAL RULE

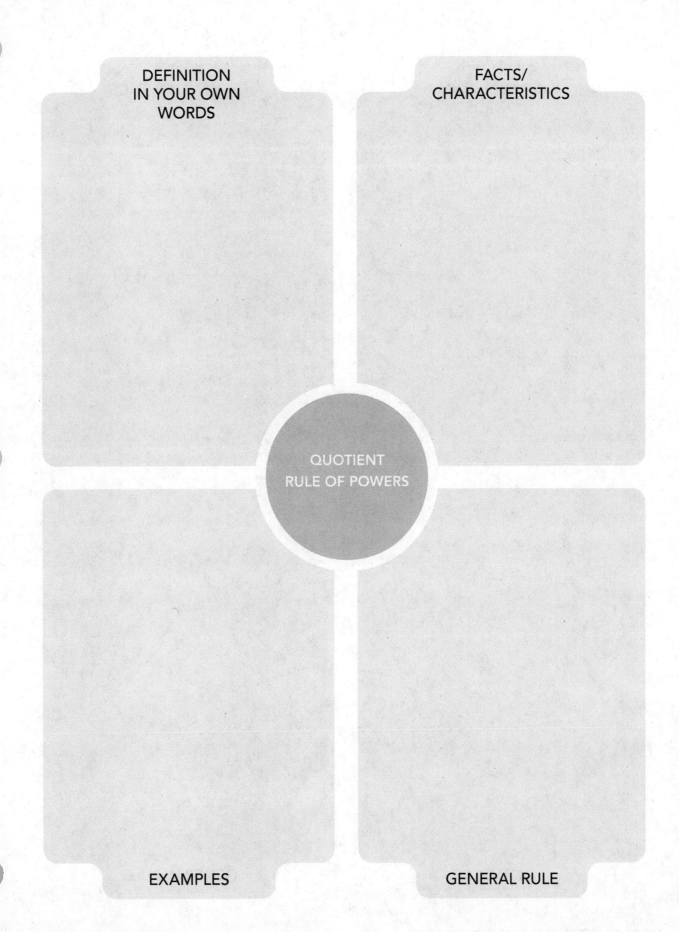

DEFINITION
IN YOUR OWN
WORDS

FACTS/
CHARACTERISTICS

QUOTIENT
RULE OF POWERS

EXAMPLES

GENERAL RULE

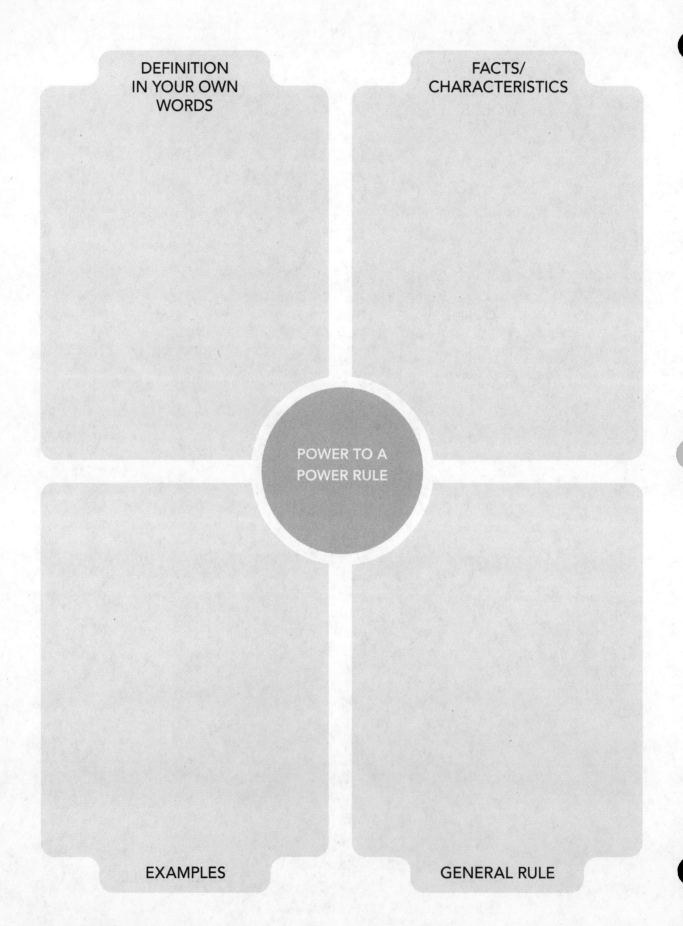

DEFINITION
IN YOUR OWN
WORDS

FACTS/
CHARACTERISTICS

POWER TO A
POWER RULE

EXAMPLES

GENERAL RULE

**DEFINITION
IN YOUR OWN
WORDS**

**FACTS/
CHARACTERISTICS**

ZERO POWER RULE

EXAMPLES

GENERAL RULE

DEFINITION
IN YOUR OWN
WORDS

FACTS/
CHARACTERISTICS

NEGATIVE
EXPONENT RULE

EXAMPLES

GENERAL RULE

Assignment

Write

In your own words write the Quotient Rule, Product Rule, and Power to a Power Rule. Use examples to illustrate your descriptions.

Remember

Negative exponents in the numerator can be moved to the denominator and become positive, $a^{-m} = \frac{1}{a^m}$, if $a \neq 0$ and $m > 0$.

The zero power of any number except for 0 is 1.

Practice

Justify each step to simplify each expression. Choose the properties from the box.

Product Rule of Powers	Power to a Power Rule	Negative Exponent Rule	Quotient Rule of Powers
Zero Power Rule	Simplify Powers	Identity Property of Multiplication	Commutative Property of Multiplication

1. $4x^5 \cdot 6x^2y^6 \cdot xy$

2. $3a^2b^3 \cdot 7ab^5 \cdot b^2$

3. $(4m^2n^5)^3$

4. $(-3x^7y^3)^5$

5. $\frac{27y^8z^5}{-3y^4z^2}$

6. $\frac{-96m^9n^2}{8m^2n^6}$

7. $-2x^5y^3 \cdot 8x^2y^{-5} \cdot x^{-9}y^2$

8. $\frac{42m^5n^3 \cdot m^4n^2}{6m^6n^5}$

Stretch

Three positive integers have a sum of 10. How can you place the integers in the square brackets to form the greatest number possible?

$([\quad]) \cdot ([\quad])^{[ ]}$

Review

1. Simplify each expression using the properties of powers.

   a. $10^4 \cdot 10^{-5}$

   b. $2^{-6} \div 2^{-2}$

2. Plot and connect the points on a coordinate plane. Use the Pythagorean theorem to determine the length of the hypotenuse.

   a. A (0, 1), B (0, 7), C (8, 1)

   b. E (1, 4), F (1, 0), G (8, 4)

3. In each set of numbers, determine which value(s) are irrational numbers.

   a. $2\frac{2}{3}, \frac{5}{11}, \pi, \sqrt{9}, \sqrt{8}$

   b. $5.333, 0.\overline{33}, 4.25, 4.\overline{23}, 4.232425\ldots$

The Big and Small of It

Scientific Notation

WARM UP

Complete each statement to make it true.

1. $15 \cdot$ _____ = 15,000

2. $2.13 \cdot$ _____ = 21,300,000

3. $1.435 \cdot 0.1 =$ _____

4. _____ $\cdot 0.001 = 0.00576$

LEARNING GOALS

- Express numbers in scientific notation.
- Express numbers in standard form.
- Compare numbers written in scientific notation.
- Interpret scientific notation that has been generated by technology.

KEY TERMS

- scientific notation
- mantissa
- characteristic
- order of magnitude

You have used properties of powers to rewrite expressions with various bases and integer exponents. How can you use powers of 10 to represent and compare very large and very small numbers?

In the Blink of an Eye

"Your childhood will be gone in the blink of an eye!"

Has anyone ever told you not to grow up too fast? Or have you heard something similar?

Have you ever thought about how short a blink is? Or how many times you blink in an hour? In a day? In a year?

1. **If the average person blinks once every 3 seconds, how many times have you blinked in your lifetime?**

Introduction to Scientific Notation

Kanye, Corinne, and Brock wanted to know how many times their entire class has blinked in their lifetimes. Each student used a different technology device: Kanye used a basic calculator, Corinne used the calculator on her phone, and Brock used a graphing calculator. There are 25 students in the class. Kanye, Corinne, and Brock decided that, on average, the students each had blinked 98,112,000 times.

> Corinne could also rotate her phone to see a display similar to the display on the graphing calculator.

1. Analyze the display on each calculator.

2.45E+09

2.4528e9

98112000*25
          2452800000

a. **What was the total number of blinks for the entire class? Which display did you use to determine the total number?**

b. **Use the total number of blinks to interpret each of the remaining displays. How are the displays similar? How are they different?**

Scientific notation
is a tool to help you
read and think about
extremely large
or small positive
numbers.

The numbers on the smaller displays represented the large number of blinks in *scientific notation*.

Scientific notation is a notation used to express a very large or a very small number as the product of two numbers:

- a number that is greater than or equal to 1 and less than 10, and
- a power of 10.

In general terms, $a \times 10^n$ is a number written in scientific notation, where *a* is greater than or equal to 1 and less than 10, and *n* is any integer. The number *a* is called the **mantissa**, and *n* is the called the **characteristic**.

Scientific notation makes it much easier to tell at a glance the *order of magnitude*. The **order of magnitude** is an estimate of size expressed as a power of ten. For example, Earth's mass has an order of magnitude of 10^{24} kilograms.

2. **Write the number of blinks from the calculator displays in scientific notation. Identify the mantissa and characteristic. What do you think the *e* in the displays means?**

3. Use your graphing or scientific calculator to explore extremely large and extremely small numbers.

a. Enter each given number into your calculator and complete the table.

Given Number	Calculator Display	What Does the Calculator Display Mean?
35,400,000,000		
60,000,000,000,000		
0.0000007		
0.000008935		

b. Describe the characteristics for extremely large numbers.

c. Describe the characteristics for extremely small numbers.

d. Describe the mantissa in each.

4. **Kanye, Corinne, Brock, and Daniel each tried to write the number 16,000,000,000 in scientific notation. Analyze each student's reasoning.**

Kanye's Method

I start with 1.6, a number that is less than 10 and greater than 1. Next, I need a power of 10. If I multiply 1.6 by 10, I get 16. Then, if I multiply by 10 again, I get 160. Multiply by 10 again, and I get 1600. So, I can just keep multiplying by 10 until I get back to the original number. I have to multiply by 10 ten times, so my power of 10 is 10^{10}. So, 16,000,000,000 in scientific notation is 1.6×10^{10}.

Brock's Method

I have to write a number greater than 1 and less than 10 multiplied by a power of 10. So, I have to multiply 1.6 by a power of 10. Since there are 9 zeros, my power of 10 will be 10^9. So, 16,000,000,000 is 1.6×10^9.

Daniel's Method

Well, that number is 16 billion. And 16 billion is 16 times 1 billion. One billion has 9 zeros, so 16,000,000,000 in scientific notation is 16×10^9.

Corinne's Method

Well, that number is 16 billion. And 16 billion is 16 times 1 billion. 16 X 1 is the same as 1.6 X 10, so 16 times 1 billion is the same as 1.6 times 10 billion. I have to multiply 10 ten times to get 10 billion, so my power of 10 is 10^{10}. That means that 16 billion in scientific notation is 1.6×10^{10}.

a. Compare Brock's and Daniel's methods.

b. Compare Kanye's and Brock's methods.

c. Compare Daniel's and Corinne's methods.

d. Of the correct methods, which method do you prefer? Why?

ACTIVITY 3.2

Scientific Notation and Large Numbers

In this activity, you will practice writing large numbers in either scientific notation or standard notation.

1. Write each number in the notation that is not given.

   a. There are approximately 3.34×10^{22} molecules in a gram of water.

   b. There are 2.5×10^{13} red blood cells in the human body.

   c. One light year is 5,880,000,000,000 miles.

   d. The speed of light is 186,000 miles per second.

2. The estimated populations, as of December 2016, of several countries are shown. Decide whether the number is written in scientific notation or standard notation. If the number is not in scientific notation, explain how you know it is not. Then, write the number in scientific notation.

   a. People's Republic of China: 1.382×10^9 people

   b. Pitcairn Islands: 50 people

   c. Australia: 24.3×10^6 people

   d. United States: 3.24×10^8 people

3. List the countries from Question 2 in order of population from least to greatest. Explain your strategy.

4. The primary U.S. currency note dispensed at an automated teller machine (ATM) is the 20-dollar bill. There are approximately 6 billion 20-dollar bills in circulation.

   a. Write the approximate number of 20-dollar bills in circulation in standard notation.

   b. Write the number of bills in scientific notation.

   c. Calculate the value of all the 20-dollar bills in circulation.

   d. Write the value you calculated in part (c) in scientific notation.

Now, let's explore writing very small numbers using scientific notation.

1. **A water molecule has an approximate length of 0.1 nanometer. One nanometer is $\frac{1}{10^7}$ of a centimeter. Complete the statements and answer the question. Write your answers as decimals.**

    a. **1 nanometer =** _____ **centimeter**

    b. **0.1 nanometer =** _____ **centimeter**

    c. **How many centimeters long is a string of 7 water molecules? Show your work.**

Just as with large numbers, scientific notation can be used to express very small numbers in a more compact form that requires less counting of zeros. The value of the number does not change, only how it is written.

2. **Each student tried to write the number 0.00065 in scientific notation. Analyze each student's reasoning.**

> ## Brock's Method
>
> I can start with 6.5, which is less than 10 and greater than 1. If I divide by 10, I get 0.65. If I divide by 10 again, I get 0.065. I just keep dividing by 10 until I get to the original number.
>
>
>
> I divided by 10 four times. So, $0.00065 = \frac{6.5}{10^4}$. But in scientific notation, I have to use multiplication, not division. That's okay because $\frac{6.5}{10^4}$ is the same as $6.5 \times \frac{1}{10^4}$. And since $\frac{1}{10^4}$ is 10^{-4}, I can write 0.00065 in scientific notation as 6.5×10^{-4}.

CORINNE'S METHOD

I CAN WRITE 0.00065 AS A FRACTION LESS THAN 1. IN WORDS, THAT DECIMAL IS SIXTY-FIVE HUNDRED THOUSANDTHS, SO I COULD WRITE IT AS $\frac{65}{100,000}$.

IF I DIVIDE BOTH THE NUMERATOR AND DENOMINATOR BY 10, I GET $\frac{65 \div 10}{100000 \div 10} = \frac{6.5}{10,000}$. AS A POWER OF 10, THE NUMBER 10,000 IS WRITTEN AS 10^4. SO THAT'S $\frac{6.5}{10^4}$, WHICH IS THE SAME AS $6.5 \times \frac{1}{10^4}$, WHICH IS THE SAME AS 6.5×10^{-4}. THAT'S THE ANSWER.

Kanye's Method

I moved the decimal point in the number to the right until I made a number greater than 1 but less than 10. So, I moved the decimal point four times to make 6.5. And since I moved the decimal point four times to the right, that's the same as multiplying 10 x 10 x 10 x 10, or 10^4. So, the answer should be 6.5×10^4.

Daniel's Method

I don't like decimals, so I moved the decimal point all the way to the right until I had a whole number. Because I moved the decimal point five times to make 65, that's the same as dividing by 10 five times. So, the answer in scientific notation should be 65×10^{-5}.

a. **Explain what is wrong with Kanye's reasoning.**

b. Explain what is wrong with Daniel's method.

c. Of the correct methods, which method do you prefer? Why?

There are names given to measurements smaller than a meter (m). You are familiar with the centimeter, the millimeter, and now the nanometer. These statements show how some small measurements relate to a meter:

- 1 centimeter (cm) = $\frac{1}{10^2}$ meter
- 1 millimeter (mm) = $\frac{1}{10^3}$ meter
- 1 micrometer (μm) = $\frac{1}{10^6}$ meter
- 1 nanometer (nm) = $\frac{1}{10^9}$ meter
- 1 picometer (pm) = $\frac{1}{10^{12}}$ meter

3. **Write each measurement as a power of 10. It is appropriate to have an expression with negative exponents in this question set.**

   a. 1 centimeter   b. 1 millimeter

   c. 1 micrometer   d. 1 nanometer

   e. 1 picometer

4. Write the radius of each type of blood vessel in standard form.

People that work with very small or very large quantities, such as scientists or astronomers, use scientific notation to make numbers more reasonable to operate on and to compare.

   a. The capillary is one of the minute blood vessels that connect arterioles and venules. The radius of a capillary is 5×10^{-3} mm.

   b. The venule is a small blood vessel that allows deoxygenated blood to return from the capillaries to the veins. The radius of a venule is 1×10^{-2} mm.

   c. The arteriole is a small blood vessel that extends and branches out from an artery and leads to capillaries. The radius of an arteriole is 5.0×10^{-1} mm.

5. Convert each measurement to meters, and then write the measurement in scientific notation.

   a. The diameter of a water molecule is 0.29 nanometers.

   b. The diameter of a red blood cell is 7 micrometers.

   c. The smallest microchip is 7 nanometers wide.

   d. A helium atom has a radius of 31 picometers.

6. Complete the table shown.

Object	Measurement	Measurement in Standard Form	Measurement in Scientific Notation
Earth	Radius in meters		6.38×10^6 m
Brachiosaurus	Mass in kilograms	77,100 kg	
Dust mite	Length in meters	0.00042 m	
Nucleus of an atom	Diameter in meters		1.6×10^{-15} m

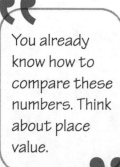

> You already know how to compare these numbers. Think about place value.

ACTIVITY 3.4

Comparing Numbers in Scientific Notation

Writing numbers in scientific notation is useful when comparing very large or very small numbers.

1. **Compare each set of large numbers written in scientific notation using the appropriate symbol: <, >, or = .**

   a. 4.5×10^4 _____ 1.5×10^4

   b. 7.6×10^{12} _____ 8.1×10^{12}

   c. 4.5×10^4 _____ 4.5×10^7

   d. 9.3×10^{15} _____ 9.3×10^{13}

   e. 7.6×10^9 _____ 5.8×10^{12}

   f. 1.9×10^8 _____ 3.2×10^4

2. Explain how to compare two large numbers using scientific notation.

3. Compare each set of small numbers written in scientific notation using the appropriate symbol: <, >, or = .

   a. 4.5×10^{-4} _____ 1.5×10^{-4}

   b. 7.6×10^{-12} _____ 8.1×10^{-12}

   c. 4.5×10^{-4} _____ 4.5×10^{-7}

   d. 9.3×10^{-15} _____ 9.3×10^{-13}

   e. 7.6×10^{-9} _____ 5.8×10^{-12}

   f. 1.9×10^{-8} _____ 3.2×10^{-4}

4. Explain how to compare two small numbers using scientific notation.

5. Describe the similarities and differences between the numbers 4.23×10^{5} and 4.23×10^{-5}.

TALK the TALK

A Rose by Any Other Name...

1. Complete the table to describe each notation.

Notation	Definition	Example
Scientific		
Standard		

Assignment

Write

Explain how to write a number expressed in standard form in scientific notation.

Remember

Scientific notation is a notation used to express a very large or very small number as the product of two numbers:
- the mantissa, which is a number greater than or equal to 1 and less than 10, and
- a power of 10, in which the exponent is called the characteristic.

Practice

1. Decide whether the number is written in scientific notation. If not, write the number in scientific notation. Explain your reasoning for each number.

   a 38.7×10^4

   b. 2.56×10^{-3}

   c. 0.025×10^{-6}

   d. 2.3^4

2. Complete the table.

Quantity	Measurement in Standard Form	Measurement in Scientific Notation
Approximate world population in number of people (December 2016)	7,433,000,000	
Time for a computer to perform an operation in seconds		3.0×10^{-10}
Average fingernail thickness in inches	0.015	
Gallons of fresh water used in the U.S. each year		2.5×10^{13}
Diameter of a very fine human hair in meters	0.000017	
Mass of Mars in tons		7.08×10^{20}
Diameter of bacteria in inches		8×10^{-6}

3. Write each number in scientific notation.

   a. There are over 29,000 grains of long-grain rice in a one-pound bag.

   b. The distance from Earth to the Moon is about 385,000,000 meters.

   c. The diameter of a red blood cell is about 0.00004 inch.

   d. A grain of salt weighs about 0.0000585 gram.

4. Write each number in standard form.

   a. There are about 1×10^5 strands of hair on the human head.

   b. The circumference of Earth at the equator is about 4.008×10^7 meters.

   c. An oxygen atom has a radius of about 4.8×10^{-11} meter.

5. Compare each set of numbers written in scientific notation using the appropriate symbol: $<$, $>$, or $=$.

   a. 6.7×10^{-8} _____ 9.5×10^{-8}

   b. 4.3×10^{12} _____ 1.3×10^{12}

   c. 3.1×10^{-4} _____ 3.1×10^{-7}

   d. 9.7×10^{15} _____ 9.7×10^{13}

   e. 2.9×10^{-11} _____ 6.8×10^{-12}

   f. 4.9×10^{-2} _____ 4.9×10^{2}

Stretch

Compare each set of numbers using the appropriate symbol: $<$, $>$, or $=$.

1. 2.478×10^4 _____ 2500

2. 2.478×10^{-4} _____ 0.00025

3. 10.5^3 _____ 5×10^3

4. 0.00012378 _____ 1.3×10^{-4}

Review

1. Simplify each expression using the properties of powers. Express your answers using only positive exponents.

   a. $\dfrac{(2^4)(2^7)(2^{-3})}{(2^{-1})(2^0)(2^8)}$

   b. $\dfrac{(-3)^4(-3)^3(-3)^{-1}}{(-3)^5(-3)^{-2}}$

2. Use the Pythagorean Theorem to answer each question.

   a. Paul and Moriah are trying to find the shortest route to their favorite restaurant. They have narrowed their search to two routes which form a right triangle. The legs of the triangle are 8 miles and 10 miles. Would it be a shorter distance traveling the legs of the triangle or the hypotenuse? Justify your answer.

   b. Eric is designing a geometric statue for an arts festival. The base of the statue is a right triangle. If the lengths of the legs of the base are 13 inches and 84 inches, how long is the hypotenuse of the base?

3. Solve each equation.

   a. $x^2 + 8 = 17$

   b. $2x^3 = 16$

How Much Larger?

Operations with Scientific Notation

WARM UP

Write each number in standard notation and in scientific notation.

1. seven thousand

2. 1.3 million

3. 2.34 billion

4. 6.85 trillion

LEARNING GOALS

- Perform operations using scientific notation.
- Compare relative sizes of numbers written in scientific notation.
- Choose units of appropriate size for measurements of very large or very small quantities.
- Interpret values in scientific notation to express how many times as much one value is than another.

You have learned about the properties of powers. How can you use these properties to perform operations with numbers expressed in scientific notation?

Eww... Eyelashes!

The average human has 90 to 150 eyelashes on each upper lid and 70–80 eyelashes on each lower lid. Each person loses approximately 1 to 4 eyelashes each day.

1. If the weight of one eyelash is approximately 0.00007 gram, approximately how many kilograms of eyelashes have you lost in your life?

ACTIVITY 4.1 — Applying the Product Rules of Powers to Scientific Notation

Before a recent class trip to a lake, Vanessa said she wanted to bring back 3 million grains of sand for a classmate who could not go on the trip. If 1 grain of sand weighs approximately 6.7×10^{-7} kg, how heavy are 3 million grains of sand?

WORKED EXAMPLE

To calculate the total weight of 3,000,000 grains of sand, you would multiply the weight of 1 grain of sand by the total number of grains of sand, or $\dfrac{0.00000067 \text{ kilograms}}{1 \text{ grain of sand}}$ (3,000,000 grains of sand).

You can use scientific notation and the Product Rules of Powers to compute this product more efficiently.

Begin by writing the numbers in scientific notation.	$(6.7 \times 10^{-7})(3 \times 10^{6})$
Apply the Associative and Commutative Properties of Multiplication.	$(6.7 \times 3)(10^{-7} \times 10^{6})$
Apply the Product Rule of Powers to powers with the same base.	$(6.7 \times 3)(10^{-7+6})$
Simplify each factor of the product.	$(20.1)(10^{-1})$
Rewrite in standard form, if desired.	2.01 kg

Three million grains of sand weigh approximately 2.01 kilograms.

1. **Suppose that a student has lost 15,000 eyelashes in his life. Use scientific notation to calculate the total weight, in kilograms, of his lost eyelashes. Write your answer in scientific notation.**

2. An ecologist estimates that it takes approximately 196,000 pounds of buried plant matter to produce one gallon of gasoline. Some energy experts estimate that the United States consumed about 140.4 billion gallons of gasoline in 2015.

   Calculate the amount of buried plant matter needed to produce the amount of gasoline consumed in 2015. Write your answer in scientific notation.

3. An oil tanker is approximately 1400 feet long. How far would 9500 oil tankers span if they were placed end to end?

   a. Calculate the approximate length of 9500 oil tankers. Write your answer in scientific notation.

Remember:
A number written in scientific notation has a mantissa greater than or equal to 1 and less than 10.

   b. What additional step is required to calculate the answer in Question 3, part (a) that was not required in Question 2?

4. Calculate each product. Express each product in scientific notation.

   a. $(3 \times 10^5)(2 \times 10^6)$ b. $(9 \times 10^4)(1 \times 10^7)$

   c. $(4.0 \times 10^8)(2.7 \times 10^4)$ d. $(5.6 \times 10^{-6})(3.5 \times 10^{15})$

5. Determine the unknown factors in each equation. Explain your reasoning.

a. $(4 \times 10^7)(? \times ?) = 8 \times 10^{12}$ b. $(? \times ?)(5 \times 10^3) = 3.5 \times 10^8$

| ACTIVITY 4.2 | Applying the Quotient Rule of Powers to Scientific Notation |

The Scoville scale measures the hotness of a chili pepper by the amount of capsaicin it contains. Capsaicin is the chemical that puts the "heat" in chili peppers. The number of Scoville heat units (SHU) indicates the amount of capsaicin present in the food. The table represents the Scoville rating for a variety of peppers.

> I wonder how much hotter a habanero pepper is than a jalapeño pepper. How could you compare the peppers?

Scoville Rating	Type
15,000,000 to 16,000,000	Pure Capsaicin
5,000,000 to 5,300,000	Law Enforcement Grade Pepper Spray
350,000 to 570,000	Red Savina Habanero
200,000 to 300,000	Habanero
70,000 to 80,000	Thai Pepper
30,000 to 50,000	Cayenne Pepper, Tabasco Pepper, some Chipotle Peppers
2500 to 8000	Jalapeño Peppers, Paprika (Hungarian)
500 to 2500	Anaheim Pepper (Mild Chile Pepper)
100 to 500	Pimento, Pepperoncini
0	No Heat, Bell Pepper

*Source: Mojave Pepper Farm's Pepper Scale

Use the values from the table to answer each question.

1. How many times hotter is the mildest law enforcement grade pepper spray than the hottest pepperoncini?

   a. First, write a ratio using the values in the table as they appear.

   b. Next, write your ratio in scientific notation.

   c. Finally, rewrite your expression using the Quotient Rule of Powers. Explain your reasoning.

   d. What does your result represent?

2. Answer each pepper heat comparison question.

   a. How many times hotter is the hottest Thai pepper than the hottest jalapeño pepper?

   b. How many times hotter is the mildest law enforcement grade pepper spray than the hottest cayenne pepper?

3. What do you notice about the results in Questions 1 and 2? Explain why this happened.

4. Answer each pepper heat comparison question.

a. How many times hotter is the hottest red savina habanero than the mildest jalapeño pepper?

b. How many times hotter is the hottest form of capsaicin than the mildest Anaheim pepper?

c. How many times hotter is the hottest cayenne pepper than the mildest jalapeño pepper?

d. How are these comparisons different from the comparisons in Questions 1 and 2?

5. Determine each quotient. Express the quotient in scientific notation.

a. $\dfrac{(6 \times 10^8)}{(2 \times 10^3)}$

b. $\dfrac{(9 \times 10^5)}{(3 \times 10^9)}$

c. $\dfrac{(8 \times 10^{-4})}{(2 \times 10^3)}$

Adding and Subtracting Numbers in Scientific Notation

The table shows the average distance of each planet from the Sun.

Planet	Average Distance from the Sun, Written in Standard Notation (kilometers)	Average Distance from the Sun, Written in Scientific Notation (kilometers)
Mercury	58,000,000	
Venus	108,000,000	
Earth	149,600,000	
Mars	228,000,000	
Jupiter	778,500,000	
Saturn	1,430,000,000	
Uranus	2,880,000,000	
Neptune	4,500,000,000	

1. **Write each distance in scientific notation in the table.**

2. Compare the distances from Mars to the Sun and Venus to the Sun.

   a. Use the standard form of the distances to determine, on average, how much farther Mars is than Venus from the Sun.

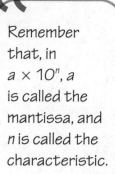

Remember that, in $a \times 10^n$, a is called the mantissa, and n is called the characteristic.

   b. Write the answer from part (a) in scientific notation.

   c. Compare the characteristics for the distances from the Sun to Mars and from the Sun to Venus. Then look at the characteristic of your answer from part (b). What do you notice?

   d. Compare the mantissas for the distances from the Sun to Mars and from the Sun to Venus. Then look at the mantissa of your answer from part (b). What do you notice?

3. Describe how to calculate the difference of two numbers written in scientific notation that have the same characteristic.

4. Compare the distances from Mars to the Sun and from Mercury to the Sun.

a. Use the standard form of the distances to determine on average how much farther Mars is from the Sun than Mercury.

b. Carlos and Tonya used scientific notation to subtract: $2.28 \times 10^8 - 5.8 \times 10^7$.

How are their methods similar?
How are their methods different?

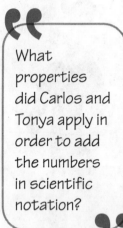

What properties did Carlos and Tonya apply in order to add the numbers in scientific notation?

Carlos

First, I rewrote 2.28×10^8 as 22.8×10^7. Then I subtracted.

$$2.28 \times 10^8 - 5.8 \times 10^7 = 22.8 \times 10^7 - 5.8 \times 10^7$$
$$= 17 \times 10^7$$
$$= 1.7 \times 10^8$$

Tonya

I rewrote 5.8×10^7 as 0.58×10^8, and then I subtracted.

$$2.28 \times 10^8 - 5.8 \times 10^7 = 2.28 \times 10^8 - 0.58 \times 10^8$$
$$= 1.7 \times 10^8$$

5. Describe how to calculate the sum or difference of two numbers written in scientific notation that have different characteristics.

6. Calculate each sum or difference using any method. Write your answer in scientific notation.

a. $3.7 \times 10^5 + 2.1 \times 10^6$

b. $2.9 \times 10^8 - 1.4 \times 10^4$

c. $2.5 \times 10^4 - 3.1 \times 10^2$

d. $9.1 \times 10^8 + 4.3 \times 10^7$

As you have seen, numbers can be written in a variety of forms. They are all just numbers, so you can operate on them once they are in similar forms. Because numbers can be written in many ways, you may need to decide what units to use when you express results of operations.

1. You are interested in determining how fast your hair grows.

   a. Which units do you think are most reasonable for this rate: nanometers per month, centimeters per month, or meters per month? Explain your reasoning.

   b. Your hairdresser says that your hair grows 6.35×10^{-6} kilometers per month. Determine how long your hair grows in 14 years. Express your answer in scientific notation, using the unit of length that you selected in part (a).

> As you work, your results may not be in scientific notation, but make sure your answer is!

2. Compare the speeds at which light and sound travel. Sound travels at a speed of 340.29 meters per second, and light travels at a speed of approximately 3×10^5 kilometers per second.

   a. Which units will you use to compare the two speeds? Explain your reasoning.

   b. How much faster is the speed of light than the speed of sound?

3. Calculate each sum, difference, product, or quotient.
   Write each answer in scientific notation.

a. $(2.35 \times 10^7) + 874{,}236$ b. $4.047 - (1.3 \times 10^{-2})$

c. $(792)(5.19 \times 10^{-5})$ d. $(6.02 \times 10^{23}) \div 12$

TALK the TALK

Operator, Operator

You have learned how to operate with numbers written in scientific notation. Can you generalize what you have learned?

1. Consider two numbers with the same characteristic: $a \times 10^n$ and $b \times 10^n$. In each case, a and b are at least 1 but less than 10, and n is an integer.

   a. Determine the product of the numbers in terms of a, b, and n.

   b. Determine the quotient of the numbers in terms of a, b, and n.

   c. Determine the sum of the numbers in terms of a, b, and n.

d. Determine the difference of the numbers in terms of *a*, *b*, and *n*.

2. Consider two numbers with the same mantissa: $a \times 10^m$ and $a \times 10^n$.

   a. Determine the product of the numbers in terms of *a*, *m*, and *n*.

   b. Determine the quotient of the numbers in terms of *a*, *m*, and *n*.

   c. Explain how to determine the sum or difference of the numbers.

3. Consider any two numbers: $a \times 10^m$ and $b \times 10^n$.

   a. Determine the product of the numbers in terms of *a*, *b*, *m*, and *n*.

   b. Determine the quotient of the numbers in terms of *a*, *b*, *m*, and *n*.

   c. Explain how to determine the sum or difference of the numbers.

Assignment

Write

Explain how multiplying and dividing numbers in scientific notation is different from adding and subtracting numbers in scientific notation.

Remember

The properties of exponents apply to numbers expressed in scientific notation.

Practice

1. As the United States has developed over the last century, Americans have used increasing amounts of electricity. The total use of electricity is measured in kilowatt-hours (kWh) and is tracked by the Department of Energy.

   a. The total use of electricity in the United States in 1902 was about 6.03 billion kilowatt-hours. Electricity use was about 595 times greater by 2000. Calculate the total use of electricity in 2000. Use scientific notation.

   b. The total use of electricity in the United States was about 0.4 trillion kilowatt-hours in 1950 and about 2.8 trillion kilowatt-hours in 1990. How many times more electricity was used in 1990 than in 1950? Use scientific notation.

   c. The total use of electricity in the U.S. decreased by 51 billion kilowatt-hours from 2007 to 2008. The electricity usage in 2007 was 3.924 trillion kilowatt-hours. Calculate the percent of decrease in electricity use by dividing the amount of decrease by the usage in 2007. Use scientific notation.

   d. What do you think may have contributed to the decrease from 2007 to 2008?

2. Calculate each sum or difference. Express your answer in scientific notation.

   a. $2.45 \times 10^7 + 4.73 \times 10^8$

   b. $9.01 \times 10^{12} - 8.67 \times 10^{11}$

   c. $5.19 \times 10^{-5} + 6.8 \times 10^{-8}$

   d. $1.714 \times 10^{-10} - 3.23 \times 10^{-12}$

3. Calculate each product. Express the product in scientific notation.

   a. $(2 \times 10^{-3})(3 \times 10^8)$

   b $(4.2 \times 10^{-4})(9.1 \times 10^{-6})$

   c. According to many scientists, Argentinosaurus is the heaviest known dinosaur. It weighed 220,000 pounds. How much would 1500 Argentinosaurus dinosaurs weigh? Use scientific notation to calculate the weight.

   d. The bee hummingbird is the world's smallest bird. It is about 0.05842 meter long. How far would 2,000,000 bee hummingbirds span if they were placed head to tail? Use scientific notation to calculate the length.

4. Calculate each quotient. Express the quotient in scientific notation.

a. $\dfrac{1.508 \times 10^7}{2.6 \times 10^3}$

b. $\dfrac{1.5 \times 10^{-7}}{5 \times 10^4}$

c. $\dfrac{8.82 \times 10^{-7}}{2.52 \times 10^{-2}}$

d. A football is about 280 millimeters long. A football field is about 100,000 millimeters long. How many footballs placed end to end would be needed to span the field? Use scientific notation to calculate the number of footballs.

Stretch

Calculate each power. Write your answer in scientific notation.

a. $(3 \times 10^2)^4$

b. $(1.7 \times 10^5)^3$

c. $(4.5 \times 10^3)^3$

d. $(1.2 \times 10^4)^6$

Review

1. Sylvia just completed a quiz on scientific notation. Score her quiz and provide her percent grade. Correct any errors.

Directions: Rewrite the numbers provided in either standard notation or scientific notation.

a. 3.4×10^8 = _3,400,000,000_

b. 8.25×10^{-3} = _0.00825_

c. 93,000,000 = _93×10^6_

d. 4.0005×10^5 = _400,050_

e. 0.000091 = _9.1×10^5_

2. Use the Pythagorean theorem to determine unknown side length. Round your answer to the nearest tenth.

a.

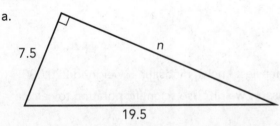

b. A right triangle has a hypotenuse with a length of 18 cm and a leg with length of 14 cm. Calculate the length of the third side.

3. Approximate each root to the nearest tenth.

a. $\sqrt{70}$

b. $\sqrt[3]{70}$

Exponents and Scientific Notation Summary

KEY TERMS

- power
- base
- exponent
- scientific notation

- mantissa
- characteristic
- order of magnitude

LESSON 1

It's a Generational Thing

An expression used to represent the product of a repeated multiplication is a power. A **power** has a base and an exponent. The **base** of a power is the expression that is used as a factor in the repeated multiplication. The **exponent** of a power is the number of times that the base is used as a factor in the repeated multiplication.

You can write a power as a product by writing out the repeated multiplication.

$$2^7 = (2)(2)(2)(2)(2)(2)(2)$$

The power 2^7 can be read as:

- "two to the seventh power."
- "the seventh power of two."
- "two raised to the seventh power."

Parentheses can change the value of expressions containing exponents. When the negative sign is not in parentheses, it's not part of the base. For example, $-1^2 = -1$, but $(-1)^2 = 1$.

Properties of Powers	Words	Rule
Product Rule of Powers	To multiply powers with the same base, keep the base and add the exponents.	$a^m \cdot a^n = a^{m+n}$
Power to a Power Rule	To simplify a power to a power, keep the base and multiply the exponents.	$(a^m)^n = a^{mn}$
Quotient Rule of Powers	To divide powers with the same base, keep the base and subtract the exponents.	$\dfrac{a^m}{a^n} = a^{m-n}$, if $a \neq 0$
Zero Power	The zero power of any number expect for 0 is 1.	$a^0 = 1$, if $a \neq 0$
Negative Exponents in the Numerator	An expression with a negative exponent in the numerator and a 1 in the denominator equals 1 divided by the power with its opposite exponent placed in the denominator.	$a^{-m} = \dfrac{1}{a^m}$, if $a \neq 0$ and $m > 0$
Negative Exponents in the Denominator	An expression with a negative exponent in the denominator and a 1 in the numerator equals the power with its opposite exponent.	$\dfrac{1}{a^{-m}} = a^m$, if $a \neq 0$ and $m > 0$

LESSON
2

Show What You Know

The properties of powers can be used to simplify numeric expressions.

For example, you can simplify the expression $\left(\dfrac{2^5}{2^4}\right)^3$.

$\left(\dfrac{2^5}{2^4}\right)^3 = (2^1)^3$ Quotient Rule of Powers

$= 2^3$ Power to a Power Powers

Scientific notation is a notation used to express a very large or a very small number as the product of two numbers:

- A number that is greater than or equal to 1 and less than 10 and
- A power of 10.

In general terms, $a \times 10^n$ is a number written in scientific notation, where a is greater than or equal to 1 and less than 10, and n is any integer. The number a is called the **mantissa**, and n is called the **characteristic**.

For example, you can write the number 16,000,000,000 in scientific notation.

$$16{,}000{,}000{,}000 = 1.6 \times 10^{10}.$$

You can also write 0.00065 in scientific notation.

$$0.00065 = 6.5 \times 10^{-4}.$$

Scientific notation makes is much easier to tell at a glance the order of magnitude. The **order of magnitude** is an estimate of size expressed as a power of ten. For example, Earth's mass has an order of magnitude of 10^{24} kilograms.

When comparing numbers written in scientific notation, start by comparing the characteristic of each number. A number with a larger characteristic has a greater value. If the two numbers have the same characteristic, the number with the greater mantissa has the greater value.

For example, 7.7×10^{12} is greater than 7.7×10^4 because $12 > 4$. Also, 9.3×10^{-3} is greater than 4.2×10^{-3} because $9.3 > 4.2$.

The properties of exponents apply to numbers expressed in scientific notation.

To multiply two numbers written in scientific notation, multiply the mantissas of each factor. Then apply the Product Rule of Powers to the powers with the same base, 10.

For example, determine the product of 6.7×10^{-7} and 2×10^6.

$(6.7 \times 10^{-7})(3 \times 10^6)$
$(6.7 \times 3)(10^{-7} \times 10^6)$
$(6.7 \times 3)(10^{-7 + 6})$
20.1×10^{-1}

To divide two numbers written in scientific notation, divide the mantissa of the dividend by the mantissa in the divisor. Then apply the Quotient Rule of Powers to the powers with the same base, 10.

For example, determine the quotient of 6×10^8 and 2×10^3.

$\dfrac{(6 \times 10^8)}{(2 \times 10^3)}$

$\left(\dfrac{6}{2}\right)\left(\dfrac{10^8}{10^3}\right)$

$\left(\dfrac{6}{2}\right)(10^{8 - 3})$

3×10^5

If you want to add or subtract numbers written in scientific notation that have the same characteristics, add or subtract the mantissas and multiply by a power of 10 with the same characteristic. If the two numbers have different characteristics, you must first rewrite either number so that the numbers have the same characteristic.

For example, determine the sum of 3.7×10^5 and 2.1×10^6.

$3.7 \times 10^5 + 2.1 \times 10^6$
$0.37 \times 10^6 + 2.1 \times 10^6$
$(0.37 + 2.1)(10^6)$
2.47×10^6

TOPIC 2
Volume of Curved Figures

Disco balls are spheres that reflect light in all different directions. They were really popular in dance clubs throughout the 1960s, 1970s, and 1980s.

Module 5: Applying Powers

TOPIC 2: VOLUME OF CURVED FIGURES

In this topic, students solve real-world and mathematical problems involving volume of cylinders, cones, and spheres. Students explore each figure in turn and determine the formula for the volume of each, they practice applying each formula, and then they solve problems requiring the use of multiple volume formulas. Students use the formulas for cylinders, cones, and spheres to determine volumes of composite figures and to compare volumes of two figures.

Where have we been?

As early as first grade, students learned about right cylinders and cones, and in grades 6 and 7, they learned to calculate volumes of prisms and pyramids and areas and circumferences of circles.

Where are we going?

This topic opens the door for students to engage in geometric design and to model real-world situations. As students study polynomial functions in high school, volumes of three-dimensional figures are applications that can be used to develop understanding of graphical characteristics and creating equations.

The Volume of a Sphere

A sphere is made up of all the points that are the same distance in three dimensions from a center point. The radius of a sphere, shown here as 4 meters, is the only measure you need to determine its volume. The volume of a sphere is given by the formula $V = \frac{4}{3}\pi r^3$.

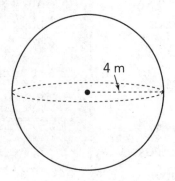

4 m

Myth: Some students are "right-brain" learners while other students are "left-brain" learners.

As you probably know, the brain is divided into two hemispheres: the left and the right. Some categorize people by their preferred or dominant mode of thinking. "Right-brain" thinkers are considered to be more intuitive, creative, and imaginative. "Left-brain" thinkers are more logical, verbal, and mathematical.

The brain can also be broken down into lobes. The occipital lobe can be found in back of the brain, and it is responsible for processing visual information. The temporal lobes, which sit above your ears, process language and sensory information. A band across the top of your head is the parietal lobe, and it controls movement. Finally, the frontal lobe is where planning and learning occurs. Another way to think about the brain is from the back to the front, where information goes from highly concrete to abstract.

Why don't we claim that some people are "back of the brain" thinkers who are highly concrete; whereas, others are "frontal thinkers" who are more abstract? The reason is that the brain is a highly interconnected organ. Each lobe hands off information to be processed by other lobes, and they are constantly talking to each other. All of us are whole-brain thinkers!

#mathmythbusted

Talking Points

You can further support your student's learning by asking questions about the work they do in class or at home. Your student is learning about the volume of cylinders, cones, and spheres.

Questions to Ask

- Does your answer make sense? Why?
- Can you show me the strategy you used to solve this problem? Do you know another way to solve it?
- Does your answer make sense? How do you know?

Key Terms

cone
A cone is a three-dimensional object with a circular or oval base and one vertex.

great circle
A great circle is the circumference of the sphere at the sphere's widest part.

Drum Roll, Please!

Volume of a Cylinder

WARM UP

Imagine a can of soup with a label.

1. Draw and describe a representation for the label if it were removed from the can.

2. Describe the sides and the top and bottom of a can of soup.

3. Describe how to determine the height of a can of soup.

4. If the radius of the top of the can is 3 inches, determine the area of the top of the can.

LEARNING GOALS

- Explore the volume of a cylinder.
- Write formulas for the volume of a cylinder.
- Use a formula to determine the volume of any cylinder.
- Use the formula for the volume of a cylinder to solve real-world problems.

KEY TERMS

- cylinder
- right cylinder
- radius of a cylinder
- height of a cylinder
- oblique cylinder

You know how to calculate the area of circles and the volume of rectangular prisms and pyramids. How can you use this knowledge to solve problems involving the volume of cylinders?

All About Cylinders

A **cylinder** is a three-dimensional object with two parallel, congruent circular bases.

A **right cylinder** is a cylinder in which the bases are circles and are aligned one directly above the other.

1. Sketch an example of a cylinder. Explain how your sketch fits the definition of a cylinder.

2. Compare your sketch with your classmates' sketches. Did everyone sketch the same cylinder? Explain how the sketches are the same or different.

The **radius of a cylinder** is the distance from the center of the base to any point on the edge of the base. The radius of a cylinder is the same on both bases.

3. Use your sketch to illustrate what is meant by "radius of the base."

The **height of a cylinder** is the length of a line segment drawn from one base to the other base, perpendicular to both bases.

4. **Use your sketch to illustrate the height of a cylinder.**

5. **Identify the radius, diameter, and height of each cylinder.**

a.
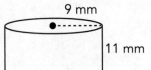
9 mm

11 mm

b.
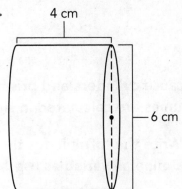
4 cm

6 cm

Volume Formula for a Cylinder

Analyze the prisms shown.

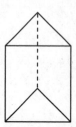 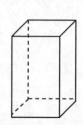 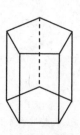 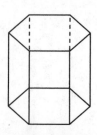

Triangular Prism   **Rectangular Prism**   **Pentagonal Prism**   **Hexagonal Prism**

1. **What pattern do you see as the number of sides of the base increases?**

Prisms and cylinders both have two bases and a constant height between the bases.

---

2. **Because cylinders and prisms are similar in composition, their volumes are calculated in similar ways.**

   a. **Write the formula for the volume of any right prism. Define all variables used in the formula.**

   b. **Make a conjecture about how you will calculate the volume of a right cylinder.**

Consider the cylinder shown. The radius of the circular base is 5 units and the height of the cylinder is 8 units.

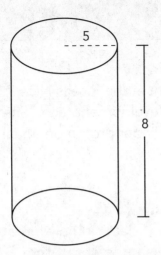
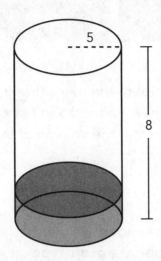

3. Suppose there is a circular disc of height 1 unit at the bottom of the cylinder.

   a. Calculate the area of the top of the circular disc.

Recall these formulas for circles.

$A = \pi r^2$

$C = 2\pi r$

   b. How many congruent circular discs would fill the cylinder? What is the volume of each disc? Explain your reasoning.

   c. Determine the total volume of the cylinder. Explain your strategy.

> How is this formula like the volume formula for prisms?

4. Write a formula for the volume of a cylinder, where V represents the volume of the cylinder, r represents the radius of the cylinder, and h represents the height of the cylinder.

The director of the marketing department at the Rice Is Nice Company sent a memo to her product development team. She requested that the volume of the new cylinder prototype equal 602.88 cm³.

1. Two members of the marketing team claim to have created appropriate prototypes, but they disagree about the dimensions of the cylinder prototype.

   Cassandra designed the cylinder prototype on the left, and Robert designed the cylinder prototype on the right. Who is correct? What would you say to Cassandra and Robert to settle their disagreement?

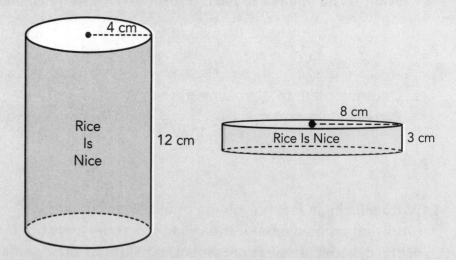

Use what you know about cylinders to solve real-world problems.

2. A circular swimming pool has a diameter of 30 feet and a height of 5 feet. What is the volume of the pool?

3. How many milliliters of liquid are needed to fill a cylindrical can with a radius of 3 centimeters and a height of 4.2 centimeters?

One milliliter is equivalent to one cubic centimeter of liquid.

4. Many newspapers are made from 100% wood. The wood used to make this paper can come from pine trees, which are typically about 60 feet tall and have diameters of about 1 foot. However, only about half of the volume of each tree is turned into paper.

Suppose it takes about 0.5 cubic inch of wood to make one sheet of paper. About how many sheets can be made from a typical pine tree? Show your work, and explain your reasoning.

5. The volume of each solid is 500 cm³. Calculate the unknown length in each figure.

a.

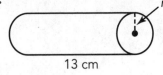

13 cm

b.

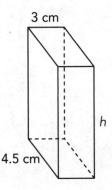

3 cm

4.5 cm

h

c.

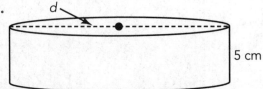

d

5 cm

Doubling Dimensions

Juan and Sandy are discussing the effect that doubling the length of the radius of the base has on the volume of a cylinder.

1. Juan insists that if the length of the radius of a cylinder doubles, the volume will double. Sandy thinks the volume will be more than double. Who is correct? Explain your reasoning.

2. Sandy and Juan wondered if the results from Question 1 were the same, regardless of the numbers they used. They created a table, hoping to see a pattern. Complete the table, and identify any patterns that you notice.

The pattern is easier to recognize if you leave your answers in terms of pi.

Cylinder Radius (cm)	Cylinder Area of Base (cm)	Cylinder Height (cm)	Cylinder Volume (cm³)
1		1	
2		1	
4		1	
8		1	

3. Juan and Sandy are also interested in the effect that doubling the height has on the volume of a cylinder.

Juan insists that if the height of a cylinder doubles, the volume will double. Sandy says the volume again will be more than double. Who is correct? Explain your reasoning.

4. Explain why the effect of doubling the length of the radius is different from the effect of doubling the height.

Oblique Cylinders

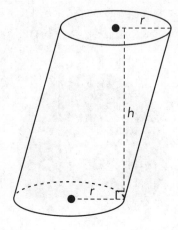

Not all cylinders are right cylinders. Consider the *oblique cylinder* shown.

1. **Explain how this cylinder is similar to and different from the right cylinders that you have explored in this lesson.**

Imagine taking cross-sections of a right cylinder and of an oblique cylinder.

2. **Compare the cross-sections that result from each slice for right cylinders and for oblique cylinders.**

   a. **slicing the cylinder parallel to its bases**

   b. **slicing the cylinder perpendicular to its bases**

3. Explain how the cross-sections created by slicing a right cylinder are related to calculating the volume of a right cylinder.

4. Apply your explanation from Question 3 to explain how to calculate the volume of an oblique cylinder.

An **oblique cylinder** is a cylinder in which the bases are parallel to each other, but they are not aligned directly above and below each other. The radius of an oblique cylinder is the radius of one of the bases, and the height is the perpendicular distance between the two bases. Its volume is calculated using the same strategies as other cylinders.

> You will learn to explain these volume strategies in high school.

5. Determine the volume of each oblique cylinder.

a.

b.

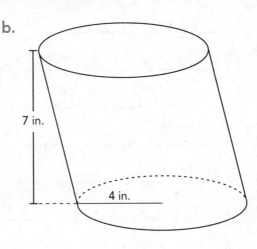

15 cm

5 cm

7 in.

4 in.

TALK the TALK 💬

The Prism Connection

Carrie was absent for the lesson on volume of a cylinder. However, she knows that the formula for the volume of a right rectangular prism can be written as $V = lwh$. Explain to Carrie how to use her knowledge of the volume of right rectangular prisms to determine the volume of a cylinder.

_____

_____

_____

_____

_____

_____

_____

_____

_____

_____

_____

_____

_____

_____

Assignment

Write

Explain the similarities and differences of right prisms, right cylinders, and oblique cylinders.

Remember

The volume of any cylinder can be calculated by multiplying the area of the circular base by the height of the cylinder.

Practice

1. Determine the volume of each cylinder. Round your answer to the nearest tenth, if necessary.

   a.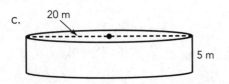
   5.5 m
   7 m

   b.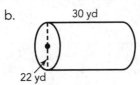
   30 yd
   22 yd

   c.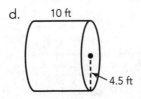
   20 m
   5 m

   d.
   10 ft
   4.5 ft

2. A cylindrical fish tank provides a 360° view. The height of the cylindrical fish tank is 30 inches, and the diameter of the base is 27.5 inches. If one US gallon is equal to approximately 231 cubic inches, calculate the amount of water the tank will hold.

3. Brittany's grandmother sends her to the store to buy a new flour canister for her kitchen. Brittany finds two canisters that she likes and is having trouble deciding which one to purchase.

   a. Calculate the volume of each canister.

   b. If the canisters cost the same, which one should Brittany purchase?

   c. A third canister has a radius of 2.5 inches and a height of 10 inches. How much less flour will this canister hold than Canister 1? Explain your reasoning.

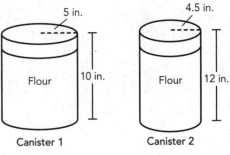

Canister 1 — 5 in., Flour, 10 in.

Canister 2 — 4.5 in., Flour, 12 in.

Stretch

Give the dimensions of a cylinder and a pentagonal prism that have the same volume and height.

Review

Use scientific notation to calcuate each product or quotient.

1. $(8.1 \times 10^{-4})(3 \times 10^9)$

2. $\dfrac{3.2 \times 10^8}{2.5 \times 10^3}$

Simplify each expression. Write your answer as a number raised to a power.

3. $(2^2)^3$

4. $-\dfrac{12^8}{12^4}$

Calculate the distance between the two given points.

5. $(-3, 8)$ and $(7, -16)$

6.

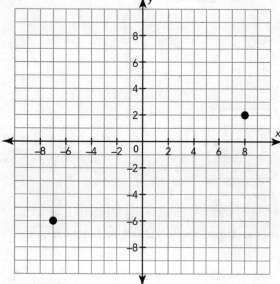

Cone of Silence

Volume of a Cone

2

WARM UP

Calculate the length of the hypotenuse given the two legs of a right triangle.

1. $r = 4.5$ cm, $s = 6$ cm

2. $a = 16$ m, $b = 24$ m

3. $h = 2.7$ in., $j = 3.9$ in.

4. $x = 0.59$ yd, $y = 1.41$ yd

LEARNING GOALS

- Explore the volume of a cone using a cylinder.
- Write formulas for the volume of a cone.
- Use the formula for the volume of a cone to solve real-world and mathematical problems.

KEY TERMS

- cone
- height of a cone

You have used what you know about prisms to determine the volume of cylinders. Is there a figure that can help you to determine the volume of cones?

All About Cones

All of the cones associated with this topic have a circular base and a vertex that is located directly above the center of the base of the cone.

A **cone** is a three-dimensional object with a circular or oval base and one vertex.

1. **Sketch an example of a cone. Explain how your sketch fits the definition of a cone.**

2. **Compare your sketch with your classmates' sketches. Did everyone sketch the same cone? Explain how the sketches are the same or different.**

3. **How does the radius of a cone compare to the radius of a cylinder? Use your sketch to illustrate the radius of the cone.**

The **height of a cone** is the length of a line segment drawn from the vertex to the base of the cone. In a right cone, this line segment is perpendicular to the base.

4. **Identify the radius, diameter, and height of each cone.**

a.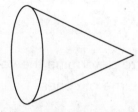

b.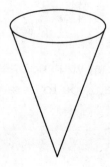

Volume of a Cone

In previous courses, you explored how the volume of a pyramid is related to the volume of a prism. Let's explore how the volume of a cone is related to the volume of a cylinder. You can use nets to investigate this relationship.

> A two-dimensional representation of a three-dimensional geometric figure is called a *net*.

1. Use the nets provided at the end of the lesson to create models of a cylinder and a cone.

   a. What is similar about the cone and cylinder formed from the nets?

   b. What do you think is true about the relationship between the cylinder and the cone?

2. Fill the cone with birdseed, and then pour the birdseed into the cylinder. Continue refilling the cone until you fill the cylinder with birdseed.

   a. How many cones of birdseed did it take to fill the cylinder?

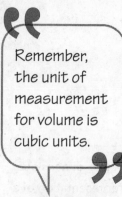

Remember, the unit of measurement for volume is cubic units.

b. Compare the amount of birdseed that you used to fill the cone and to fill the cylinder. In other words, compare the volume of the cone to the volume of the cylinder. What fraction best describes this ratio?

c. If you know the volume of the cylinder, how could you determine the volume of the cone?

3. Use a centimeter ruler to measure the length of the radius and height of the cylinder.

a. Calculate the volume of the cylinder.

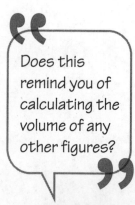

Does this remind you of calculating the volume of any other figures?

b. Using the volume of the cylinder, calculate the volume of the cone.

Volume Formula for a Cone

Analyze the pyramids shown.

1. **What pattern do you see as the number of sides of the base increases?**

Triangular Pyramid

Because cones and pyramids are similar in composition, their volumes are calculated in similar ways.

2. **Write the formula for the volume of any right pyramid and explain how it relates to your investigation with the nets.**

Rectangular Pyramid

3. **Use the formula for the volume of a pyramid to write a formula for the volume of a cone. Define all variables used in the formula.**

Pentagonal Pyramid

4. **Write a second formula for the volume of a cone, where V represents the volume, r represents the radius of the base, and h represents the height.**

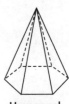

Hexagonal Pyramid

5. **Which of the two formulas do you prefer? Explain your reasoning.**

Use what you know about the volume of a cone to solve
each problem.

1. Joel owns a frozen yogurt and fruit smoothie shop. He just
   placed an order for cones, and the order contains three
   different sizes of cones. He wants to know the volume of each
   cup to help him determine how much to charge for each cone.

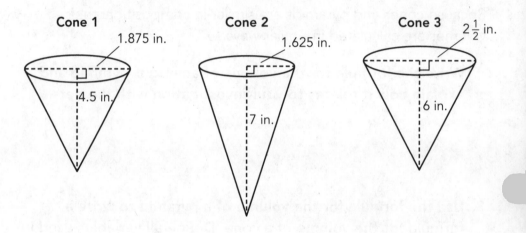

a. Predict which cone has the greatest volume.
   Explain your reasoning.

b. Calculate the volume of each cone.

c. If Joel's market research reveals that he should charge
   $3.75 for the smallest cone, what prices would you
   propose for the other two cones? Explain your reasoning.

2. Mark and Alison are working on their homework and disagree on the volume of the cone shown.

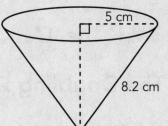

Mark says that the volume of the cone is $V = \frac{1}{3}\pi(5)^2(8.2) \approx 214.68 \text{ cm}^3$.
Alison argues that 8.2 cm is not the height of the cone, so they need to calculate the height before determining the volume. She says that the volume is $V = \frac{1}{3}\pi(5)^2(6.5) \approx 170.17 \text{ cm}^3$.
Who's correct? Explain your reasoning.

3. Calculate the volume of each cone. Round your answers to the nearest hundredth, if necessary.

a.

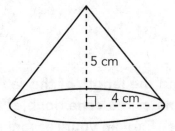

b.

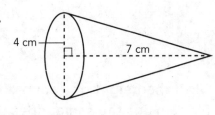

c.

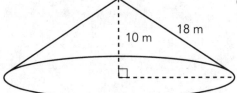

d.

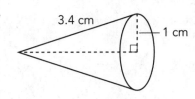

4. Use the formula for the volume of a cone to solve for each unknown dimension.

a. $V = 3042 \text{ cm}^3$, $d = 25.2 \text{ cm}$, $h = $ _____

b. $V = 25\pi \text{ in.}^3$, $h = 12 \text{ in.}$, $r = $ _____

TALK the TALK

The Doubling Effect

1. If the length of the radius of a cone doubles and the height remains the same, does the volume of the cone double? If not, how does the volume change? Explain your reasoning.

2. If the height of a cone doubles and the length of the radius remains the same, does the volume of the cone double? If not, how does the volume change? Explain your reasoning.

Cylinder Net

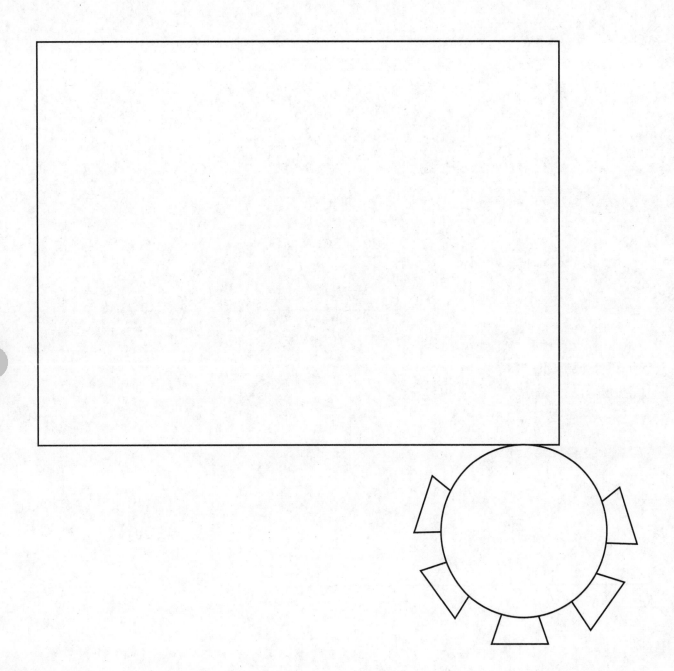

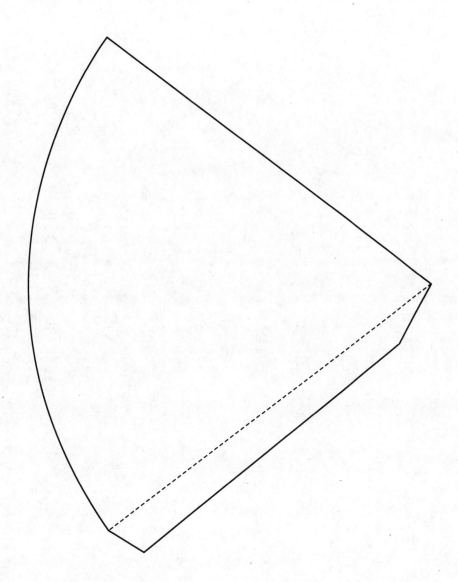

Assignment

Write

Explain when you need to use the Pythagorean Theorem to calculate the volume of a cone.

Remember

The volume of a cone is one-third the volume of the cylinder with the same base and height as the cone.

Practice

1. Determine the volume of each cone. Round your answer to the nearest tenth, if necessary.

a.

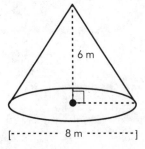

6 m

[- - - - - - - 8 m - - - - - - -]

b.

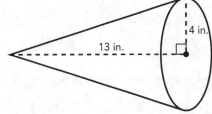

13 in.

4 in.

c.

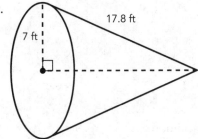

17.8 ft

7 ft

d.

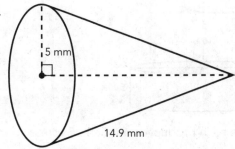

5 mm

14.9 mm

2. A company sells two sizes of cone-shaped party hats. The smaller hat has a radius of 6 cm and a volume of 376.8 cm³. The larger hats are double the volume of the smaller hats but have the same size radius. Determine the dimensions of the larger hats.

3. Cara asked her parents to make a piñata for her birthday party. Her parents decided to make the piñata in the shape of her favorite dessert, an ice cream cone. They stuffed only the cone portion of the piñata. The height of the cone is 34 inches, and the diameter of the base is 24 inches. (Note: 144 square inches equal 1 square foot, and 1728 cubic inches equals 1 cubic foot.) Calculate the amount of space (cubic feet) in the cone that will be filled with goodies.

Stretch

The frustum of a cone is the portion of a cone that remains after its upper part has been cut off by a plane parallel to its base. Calculate the volume of the frustum shown.

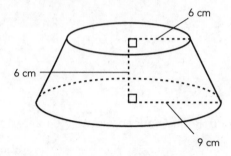

Review

Calculate the volume of each cylinder. Round your answer to the nearest tenth, if necessary.

1.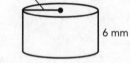
   4 mm

   6 mm

2. 16 ft

   5 ft

Determine each product or quotient. Express your answer in scientific notation.

3. $\frac{2.4 \times 10^4}{8 \times 10^{-4}}$

4. $(4.82 \times 10^8)(1.5 \times 10^{-5})$

Rewrite each expression without exponents.

5. $2^5 \cdot 2^{-2}$

6. $(10^2)^3 \cdot (-10)^2$

Pulled in All Directions

Volume of a Sphere

WARM UP

In June 2007, 7-year-old Jake Lonsway broke a world record, building the world's largest plastic wrap ball. It took him 8 months to make the ball, which weighed 281.5 pounds. The circumference of the ball was 138 inches.

1. Calculate the length of the radius and diameter of Lonsway's ball of plastic wrap. Use 3.14 for π.

2. Do you think a ball twice this size would weigh twice as much? Explain your reasoning.

LEARNING GOALS

- Identify a formula for the volume of a sphere.
- Use a formula to determine the volume of spheres in mathematical and real-world contexts.
- Use the formula for the volume of a sphere to determine an unknown length of a sphere radius or diameter.

KEY TERMS

- sphere
- center of a sphere
- radius of a sphere
- diameter of a sphere
- great circle

You have learned and applied volume formulas for a variety of different solids. In this lesson, you will learn and apply the formula for the volume of a sphere. How can you use the formula to determine both volumes and lengths of radii of spheres?

Getting to Know Spheres

A **sphere** is the set of all points in three dimensions that are the same distance from a given point called the **center of a sphere**. Like a circle, a sphere has radii and diameters. A segment drawn from the center of the sphere to a point on the sphere is called a **radius of a sphere**. A segment drawn between two points on the sphere that passes through the center is a **diameter of a sphere**. The length of a diameter is twice the length of a radius. A **great circle** is the circumference of the sphere at the sphere's widest part.

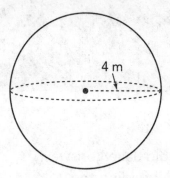

4 m

1. **List all of the things that you know to be true about this sphere.**

ACTIVITY 3.1 Modeling the Volume of a Sphere

Use the modeling clay and paper provided by your teacher to complete each step.

- Make a sphere using the clay. Measure and record the diameter of the sphere.

- Cut a long strip of paper so that its height matches the height of the sphere.

- Wrap the paper tightly around the sphere and tape the paper to make a sturdy cylinder with no bases.

- Squish the clay sphere so that it molds to the bottom of the cylinder.

- Mark the height of the clay in the cylinder with a marker.

1. **Complete the first row of the table with the data from your sphere. Then, complete the other rows using data from three other classmates.**

Sphere	Diameter	Cylinder Height	Height of Squished Sphere in Cylinder	Height of Squished Sphere ———————— Height of Cylinder
My Sphere				
Classmate A				
Classmate B				
Classmate C				

2. What do you notice about the ratio of the height of the squished sphere to the height of the cylinder?

3. What is the relationship between the volume of the sphere and the volume of the cylinder?

_____

Recall that the formula for the volume of a cylinder is $V = \pi r^2 h$.

_____

4. What is the height, h, of the cylinder in terms of the radius, r, of the sphere? Explain your reasoning.

5. Use this relationship and the formula for the volume of a cylinder to write a formula that describes the volume of the sphere in terms of r.

Applying the Formula for the Volume of a Sphere

Now that you know how to calculate the volume of a sphere, use the formula to solve each problem. Use 3.14 for π.

1. Earth has a diameter of approximately 7926 miles.

   a. Determine the length of the radius of Earth.

   b. Determine the volume of Earth.

2. The circumference of an NBA basketball ranges from 29.5 to 30 inches.

   a. Calculate the approximate length of the radius of a basketball with a circumference of 30 inches.

   b. Calculate the approximate volume of a basketball with a circumference of 30 inches.

3. The volume of a Major League baseball is 12.77 cubic inches.

   a. Calculate the approximate length of the radius of a Major League baseball.

   b. Calculate the approximate circumference of a Major League baseball.

4. Built in the 1950s by the Stamp Collecting Club at Boy's Town, the World's Largest Ball of Postage Stamps is very impressive. The solid ball has a diameter of 32 inches, weighs 600 pounds, and consists of 4,655,000 postage stamps.

   Calculate the volume of the world's largest ball of postage stamps.

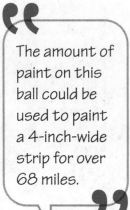

The amount of paint on this ball could be used to paint a 4-inch-wide strip for over 68 miles.

5. The world's largest ball of paint resides in Alexandria, Indiana. The ball began as a baseball. People began coating the ball with layers of paint. Imagine this baseball with over 21,140 coats of paint on it! The baseball originally weighed approximately 5 ounces and now weighs more than 2700 pounds. Painting this baseball has gone on for more than 32 years, and people are still painting it today.

   When the baseball had 20,500 coats of paint on it, the circumference along the great circle of the ball was approximately 133 inches. Each layer is approximately 0.001037 inches thick.

   Calculate the volume of the world's largest paint ball.

6. The world's largest disco ball hangs from a fixed point and is powered by a 5-ton hydraulic rotator. It weighs nearly 1.5 tons with a volume of approximately 67 cubic meters. Approximately 8000 100-square-centimeter mirror tiles and over 10,000 rivets were used in its creation.

Calculate the length of the radius of the world's largest disco ball.

7. For over seven years, John Bain spent his life creating the world's largest rubber band ball. It is solid to the core with rubber bands. Each rubber band was individually stretched around the ball, creating a giant rubber band ball. The weight of the ball is over 3,120 pounds, and the circumference is 15.1 feet.

Calculate the volume of the world's largest rubber band ball.

There are 850,000 rubber bands in the ball, and the cost of the materials was approximately $25,000!

8. The world's largest ball of twine is in Darwin, Minnesota. It weighs 17,400 pounds and was created by Francis A. Johnson. He began this pursuit in March 1950. He spent four hours a day, every day wrapping the ball. It took Francis 39 years to complete. Upon completion, it was moved to a circular open air shed on his front lawn for all to view.

If the volume of the world's largest ball of twine is 7234.56 cubic feet, determine the length of the diameter.

At some point, the ball had to be lifted with a crane to continue proper wrapping.

TALK the TALK

Locker Room Math

Young people often attempt to break world records. Jessica is no exception. Today her math class studied the volume of a sphere, and she had a great idea. After working out the math, Jessica told her best friend Molly that they could stuff 63 inflated regulation-size basketballs into a school locker. The rectangular locker is 6 feet high, 20 inches wide, and 20 inches deep. The radius of one basketball is 4.76 inches. Molly also did the math and said that only 28 basketballs would fit.

1. **How did Molly and Jessica compute their answers? Who's correct? Explain your reasoning.**

Assignment

Write

Describe the similarities and differences between each pair of terms.
1. radius of the sphere and diameter of the sphere
2. radius of the sphere and center of the sphere

Remember

The volume of a sphere is given by the formula $V = \frac{4}{3}\pi r^3$, where r represents the radius of the sphere.

Practice

Solve each problem. Use 3.14 for π.

1. The diameter of a small red beach ball is 8 inches. Calculate the volume of the red beach ball to the nearest whole number.

2. The diameter of a large blue beach ball is 16 inches. Calculate the volume of the blue beach ball to the nearest whole number.

3. Spaceship Earth is the most recognizable structure at Epcot Center at Disney World in Orlando, Florida. The ride is a geodesic sphere made up of thousands of small triangular panels. The circumference of Spaceship Earth is 518.1 feet. Determine its approximate volume.

4. The Oriental Pearl Tower in Shanghai, China, is a 468-meter high tower with 11 spheres along the tower. Two spheres are larger than the rest and house meeting areas, an observation deck, and a revolving restaurant. The lower of the two larger spheres has a radius of 25 meters, and the higher sphere has a radius of 22.5 meters. What is the approximate total volume of the two largest spheres on the Oriental Pearl Tower?

5. A model of Earth is located 7600 meters from the Globe Arena in Sweden's solar system model. The volume of the model is approximately 3052.08 cubic centimeters. What is the length of the radius of the Earth model?

6. The Montreal Biosphere is a geodesic dome that surrounds an environmental museum in Montreal, Canada. The dome has a volume of 6,132,812.5 cubic feet. The structure is 75% of a full sphere. What is the length of its diameter?

Stretch

A typical orange has 10 segments and is composed of about 87% water. Suppose an orange has a diameter of 3 inches. What is the volume of water in each segment?

Review

Determine the volume of each cone described. Use 3.14 for π.

1. Cone with a radius of 4.1 cm and a height of 10 cm

2. Cone with a diameter of 8 in. and a height of 5.03 in.

Determine each quotient. Write each quotient as a power and in standard form.

3. $\dfrac{6^4}{6^5}$

4. $\dfrac{9^{-1}}{9^{-2}}$

Determine each quotient. Write your response using scientific notation.

5. $\dfrac{(6.4 \times 10^8)}{(2.0 \times 10^2)}$

6. $\dfrac{(1.6 \times 10^3)}{(2.5 \times 10^6)}$

Silos, Frozen Yogurt, and Popcorn

4

Volume Problems with Cylinders, Cones, and Spheres

WARM UP

You have been asked to supply the ice cream for a birthday party. Assume that each person attending the party will eat one ice cream cone. The local grocery store sells ice cream in rectangular half-gallon containers. Each container is 6.75 inches in length, 5 inches in height, and 3.5 inches in width. Your plan is to put two scoops of ice cream in each cone. Each scoop is a sphere with a radius of 1 inch.

1. What is the volume of one scoop of ice cream?

2. If 30 people attended the birthday party, how many half-gallons of ice cream should you buy?

LEARNING GOALS

- Use formulas for the volume of a cone, cylinder, and sphere to solve real-world and mathematical problems.
- Compare volumes of cones, cylinders, and spheres.

You have learned the formulas for the volume of a cylinder, the volume of a cone, and the volume of a sphere. How can you reason with these formulas separately and together to solve problems?

Formula Review

By now, you have determined some formulas for prisms, pyramids, cylinders, cones, and spheres.

1. Write the formula for the volume of each solid. Use V for volume, B for area of a base, h for height, r for radius, and π for pi.

Solid	Model	Volume Formula
Rectangular Prism		
Triangular Prism		
Rectangular Pyramid		
Triangular Pyramid		
Cylinder		
Cone		
Sphere		

Cylinder and Half-Sphere Problem

A silo is used to store grain that farm animals eat during the winter months. The top of the silo is a hemisphere (a half-sphere) with a radius of 8 feet. The cylindrical body of the silo shares the same radius as the hemisphere and has a height of 40 feet.

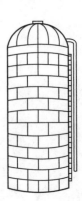

A truck hauling grain to the silo has a rectangular container attached to the back that is 8 feet in length, 5 feet in width, and 4 feet in height.

1. **Determine the number of truckloads of grain required to fill an empty silo.**

The word *fill* is often used to describe the volume of a solid. Consider how much you can fill the cones described in each question. Use 3.14 for π.

1. A frozen yogurt shop advertises that their frozen yogurt is now sold in cones that hold 25% more frozen yogurt than the old cones. The old cone has a radius of 3.75 centimeters and a height of 11 centimeters. The length of the radius of the new cone is the same as the length of the radius of the old cone. What is the height of the new cone?

2. A frozen yogurt cone is 12 centimeters in height and has a diameter of 6 centimeters. A scoop of frozen yogurt is placed on the wide end of the cone. The scoop is a sphere with a diameter of 6 centimeters.

   If the scoop of frozen yogurt melts into the cone, will the cone overflow? Explain your reasoning.

If you were to make a cylinder using a piece of paper, is the volume the same no matter which way you roll the paper?

Use the paper provided by your teacher to complete an investigation of cylinder volume.

- Roll one piece of paper along its longer side. This will form a cylinder (Cylinder A) with no bases that is tall and narrow. Tape along the edges without overlapping the sides of the paper.

- Roll a second piece of paper of the same size but a different color along its shorter side. This will form a cylinder (Cylinder B) with no bases that is short and wide. Tape along the edges without overlapping the sides.

1. **Do you think that the two cylinders have the same volume? Make a conjecture and explain your thinking.**

2. **Stand Cylinder B upright on your desk with Cylinder A inside it. Pour centimeter cubes into Cylinder A until it is full. Carefully lift Cylinder A so that the centimeter cubes fall into Cylinder B. Describe what happens.**

3. Consider your prediction about the volumes of Cylinder A and Cylinder B.

   a. Was your prediction correct? How do you know?

   b. If your prediction was incorrect, why do you think what actually happened was different from your prediction?

4. Measure the dimensions of the tall, narrow cylinder and enter them in the table as measures for Cylinder A. Then, measure the dimensions of the short, wide cylinder and enter them in the table as measures for Cylinder B.

Dimension	Cylinder A	Cylinder B
Height (in.)		
Diameter (in.)		
Radius (in.)		

5. Calculate the volumes of the cylinders.

6. By how much would you have to decrease the height of Cylinder B to make the volumes of the two cylinders equal?

Consider the popcorn containers: one is a cylindrical tub and the other is conical. When they are full of popcorn, the containers hold the same amount of popcorn.

1. Calculate the volume of the cylindrical tub.

2. If the height of the conical container is 10.1 inches, what is the length of the radius of the cone?

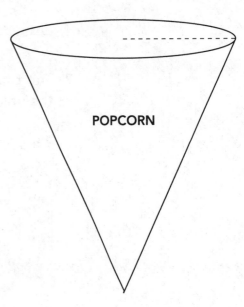

3. If the length of the radius of the conical container is the same as the length of the radius of the cylindrical tub, what is the height of the cone?

TALK the TALK

Composite Solids

Use what you know about the volume of curved figures to solve each problem. Use 3.14 for π.

1. The building shown is composed of a cylinder and a cone. Determine the volume of this building.

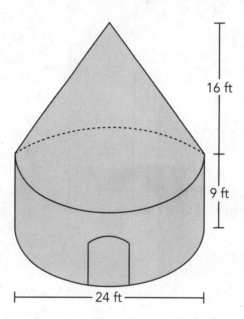

16 ft

9 ft

24 ft

2. The top of this model forms a half-sphere. Determine the volume of this model.

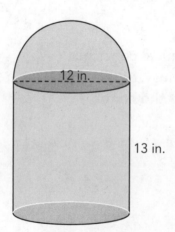

12 in.

13 in.

Assignment

Write

Describe the relationships among the volumes of a cylinder, cone, and sphere that have the same height and radius.

Remember

The formula for the volume of a cylinder is $\pi r^2 h$.

The formula for the volume of a cone is $\frac{1}{3}\pi r^2 h$.

The formula for the volume of a sphere is $\frac{4}{3}\pi r^3$.

Practice

Solve each problem. Use 3.14 for π.

1. Veronica is making a large sphere-shaped piñata for a party. The piñata is going to be 2 feet in diameter. In order to know how much candy she will need to fill the piñata, she needs to know the volume of the piñata. Calculate the volume of this large piñata.

2. A jeweler sold a string of fifty 8-millimeter pearls. He needs to choose a box to put them in. Which box should the jeweler choose?

3. The drinking glass is not a cylinder, but is actually part of a cone. Determine the volume of the glass.

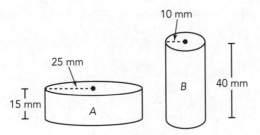

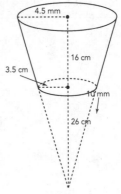

4. A tennis ball company is designing a new can to hold 3 tennis balls. They want to waste as little space as possible. How much space does each can waste? Which can design should they choose?

5. A candle company makes pillar candles, spherical candles, and conical candles. They have an order for 3 pillar, 2 spherical, and 1 conical candle. Wax is sold in large rectangular blocks. What are the possible dimensions for a wax block that could be used to fill this order?

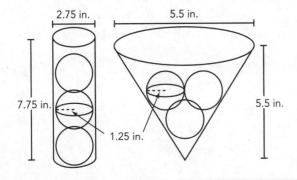

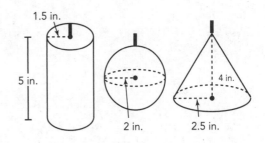

6. An ice cream shop sells cones with a volume of 94.2 cubic centimeters. They want to double the volume of their cones without changing the diameter of the cone so that the ice cream scoop will stay on top of the cone. What should the dimensions of the new cone be if the old cone had a height of 10 centimeters?

Stretch

A container in the shape of a half-sphere is on top of a cylinder. The container has a volume of 360π cubic inches. The total height of the container is the same as the diameter of the half-sphere. What is the diameter of the half-sphere?

Review

Calculate each volume. Use 3.14 for π. Round to the nearest hundredth.

1. What is the volume of a sphere with a diameter of 8.5 inches?
2. What is the volume of a sphere with a radius of 9 millimeters?

3.   6 m

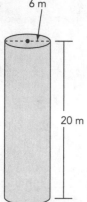

20 m

4.

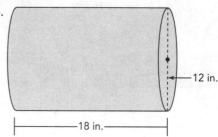

12 in.

18 in.

Determine each sum. Write each sum in scientific notation.

5. $4.1 \times 10^3 + 3.5 \times 10^4$

6. $9.9 \times 10^5 + 2.9 \times 10^2$

Volume of Curved Figures Summary

KEY TERMS

- cylinder
- right cylinder
- radius of a cylinder
- height of a cylinder
- oblique cylinder
- cone
- height of a cone
- sphere
- center of a sphere
- radius of a sphere
- diameter of a sphere
- great circle

LESSON 1

Drum Roll, Please!

A **cylinder** is a three-dimensional object with two parallel, congruent circular bases. A **right cylinder** is a cylinder in which the bases are circles and are aligned one directly above the other.

The **radius of a cylinder** is the distance from the center of the base to any point on the edge of the base. The length of the radius of a cylinder is the same on both bases. The **height of a cylinder** is the length of a line segment drawn from one base to the other base, perpendicular to both bases.

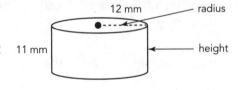

The volume of any cylinder can be calculated by multiplying the area of the circular base by the height of the cylinder. The formula for the area of a circle is $A = \pi r^2$, so the formula for the volume of a cylinder is $V = \pi r^2 h$.

For example, calculate the volume of the given cylinder.

$$V = \pi r^2 h$$
$$= \pi (12^2)(11)$$
$$\approx 4976.28 \text{ cubic millimeters}$$

Doubling only the length of the radius of a cylinder quadruples the volume of the cylinder, while doubling only the height doubles the volume.

Not all cylinders are right cylinders. An **oblique cylinder** is a cylinder in which the bases are parallel to each other, but they are not aligned directly above and below each other. The radius of an oblique cylinder is the radius of one of the bases, and the height is the perpendicular distance between the two bases. Its volume is calculated using the same strategies as other cylinders.

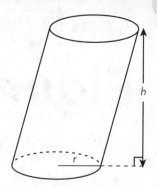

Cone of Silence

A **cone** is a three-dimensional object with a circular or oval base and one vertex. The **height of a cone** is the length of a line segment drawn from the vertex to the base of the cone. In a right cone, this line segment is perpendicular to the base.

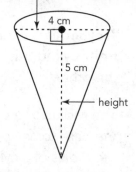

The volume of a cone is one-third the volume of the cylinder with the same base and height as the cone. Therefore, the formula for the volume of a cone is $V = \frac{1}{3}\pi r^2 h$.

For example, calculate the volume of the given cone.

$$V = \frac{1}{3}\pi r^2 h.$$

$$= \frac{1}{3}\pi\left(\frac{4}{2}\right)^2 (5)$$

$$\approx 20.94 \text{ cubic centimeters}$$

Pulled in All Directions

A **sphere** is the set of all points in three dimensions that are the same distance from a given point called the **center of a sphere**. Like a circle, a sphere has radii and diameters. A segment drawn from the center of the sphere to a point on the sphere is called a **radius of a sphere**. A segment drawn between two points on the sphere that passes through the center is a **diameter of a sphere**. The length of a diameter is twice the length of a radius. A **great circle** is the circumference of the sphere at the sphere's widest part.

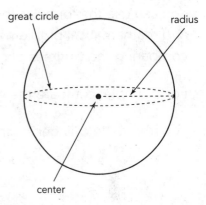

great circle

radius

center

The volume of a sphere is given by the formula $V = \frac{4}{3}\pi r^3$, where r represents the length of the radius of the sphere.

For example, calculate the volume of a sphere with a radius length of 4.5 inches.

$$V = \frac{4}{3}\pi r^3$$
$$= \frac{4}{3}\pi(4.5)^3$$
$$\approx 381.7 \text{ cubic inches}$$

You can use the formulas for the volume of a cone, cylinder, and sphere to solve real-world and mathematical problems, including determining the volume of composite figures and comparing the volumes of cones, cylinders, and spheres.

For example, compare the volumes of the cylinder, sphere and cone.

Volume of the cylinder $= \pi r^2 h$

$\qquad = \pi(2)^2(5)$

$\qquad \approx 62.83$ cubic inches

Volume of the sphere $= \frac{4}{3}\pi r^3$

$\qquad = \frac{4}{3}\pi(3)^3$

$\qquad \approx 113.1$ cubic inches

Volume of the cone $= \frac{1}{3}\pi r^2 h$

$\qquad = \frac{1}{3}\pi(3)^2(4)$

$\qquad \approx 37.7$ cubic inches

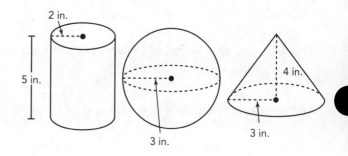

The volume of the sphere is the greatest, and the volume of the cone is the least.

Glossary

absolute value function

An absolute value function is a function that can be written in the form $y = |x|$, where x is any number or expression.

alternate exterior angles

Alternate exterior angles are angles formed when a transversal intersects two other lines. These angle pairs are on opposite sides of the transversal and are outside the other two lines.

Example

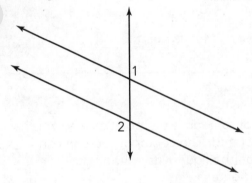

Angles 1 and 2 are alternate exterior angles.

alternate interior angles

Alternate interior angles are angles formed when a transversal intersects two other lines. These angle pairs are on opposite sides of the transversal and are between the other two lines.

Example

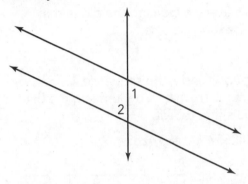

Angles 1 and 2 are alternate interior angles.

angle of rotation

The angle of rotation is the amount of rotation, in degrees, about a fixed point, the center of rotation.

Example

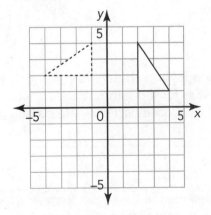

The angle of rotation is 90° counterclockwise about the origin (0, 0).

Angle-Angle Similarity Theorem

The Angle-Angle Similarity Theorem states that if two angles of one triangle are congruent to the corresponding angles of another triangle, then the triangles are similar.

association

A pattern or relationship identified in a scatter plot of a two-variable data set is called an association.

— B —

bar notation

Bar notation is used to indicate the digits that repeat in a repeating decimal.

Example

In the quotient of 3 and 7, the sequence 428571 repeats. The numbers that lie underneath the bar are the numbers that repeat.

$$\frac{3}{7} = 0.4285714285714... = 0.\overline{428571}$$

base

The base of a power is the factor that is multiplied repeatedly in the power.

Examples

$$2^3 = 2 \times 2 \times 2 = 8 \qquad 8^0 = 1$$

↑ base   ↑ base

bivariate data

When you collect information about two separate characteristics for the same person, thing, or event, you have collected bivariate data.

break-even point

When one line represents the cost of an item and the other line represents the income from selling the item, the point of intersection is called the break-even point.

— C —

categorical data

Categorical data, or qualitative data, are data for which each piece of data fits into exactly one of several different groups or categories.

Examples

Animals: lions, tigers, bears, etc.

Colors: blue, green, red, etc.

center of dilation

The point from which a dilation is generated is called the center of dilation.

Example

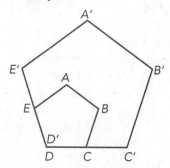

The center of dilation is point *D*.

center of rotation

The center of rotation is the point around which a figure is rotated. The center of rotation can be a point on the figure, inside the figure, or outside the figure.

Example

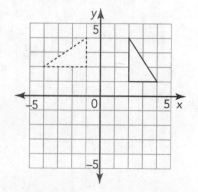

The figure has been rotated 90° counterclockwise about the center of rotation, which is the origin (0, 0).

center of the sphere

The given point from which the set of all points in three dimensions are the same distance is the center of the sphere.

Example

Point C is the center of the sphere.

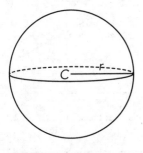

characteristic

In the expression $a \times 10^n$, the variable n is called the characteristic.

Example

$6.1 \times 10^5 = 610,000$

↑
characteristic

closed

A set of numbers is said to be closed under an operation if the result of the operation on two numbers in the set is a defined value also in the set.

Example

The set of integers is closed under the operation of addition because for every two integers a and b, the sum $a + b$ is also an integer.

collinear points

Collinear points are points that lie in the same straight line.

Example

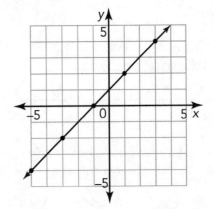

All the points on the graph are collinear points.

cone

A cone is a three-dimensional object with a circular or oval base and one vertex.

Example

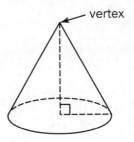

congruent angles

Congruent angles are angles that are equal in measure.

congruent figures

Figures that have the same size and shape are congruent figures. If two figures are congruent, all corresponding sides and all corresponding angles have the same measure.

congruent line segments

Congruent line segments are line segments that have the same length.

consistent system

Systems that have one or an infinite number of solutions are called consistent systems.

constant function

When the y-value of a function does not change, or remains constant, the function is called a constant function.

constant interval

When a function is constant for some values of the independent variable, it is said to have a constant interval.

Example

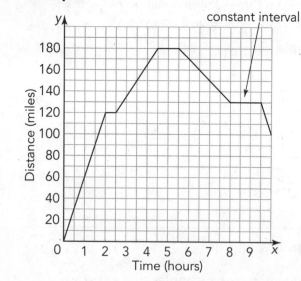

constant of proportionality

In a proportional relationship, the ratio of all y-values to their corresponding x-values is constant. This specific ratio, $\frac{y}{x}$, is called the constant of proportionality. Generally, the variable k is used to represent the constant of proportionality.

continuous

A continuous graph is a graph with no breaks in it.

Examples

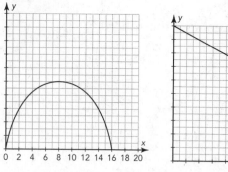 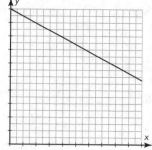

converse

The converse of a theorem is created when the if-then parts of that theorem are exchanged.

Example

Triangle inequality Theorem:

If a polygon is a triangle, then the sum of any two of its side lengths is always greater than the length of the third side.

Converse of Triangle Inequality Theorem:

If you have three side lengths, and the sum of any two of the side lengths is greater than the third side length, then the side lengths can form a triangle.

Converse of the Pythagorean Theorem

The Converse of the Pythagorean Theorem states that if the sum of the squares of the two shorter sides of a triangle equals the square of the longest side, then the triangle is a right triangle.

Example

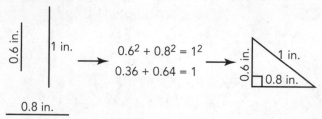

corresponding angles

Corresponding angles are angles that have the same relative positions in geometric figures.

Example

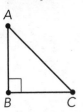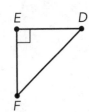

Angle B and Angle E are corresponding angles.

corresponding sides

Corresponding sides are sides that have the same relative positions in geometric figures.

Example

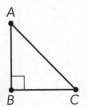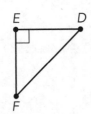

Sides AB and DE are corresponding sides.

cube root

A cube root is one of 3 equal factors of a number.

Example

The cube root of 125, $\sqrt[3]{125}$, is 5, because $5 \times 5 \times 5 = 125$.

cubic function

A cubic function is a function that can be written in the form $y = ax^3 + bx^2 + cx + d$, where each coefficient or constant a, b, c, and d is a real number and a is not equal to 0.

cylinder

A cylinder is a three-dimensional object with two parallel, congruent circular bases.

Examples

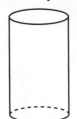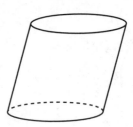

—— D ——

decreasing function

When the value of a dependent variable decreases as the independent variable increases, the function is called a decreasing function.

diagonal

In a three-dimensional figure, a diagonal is a line segment connecting any two non-adjacent vertices.

Example

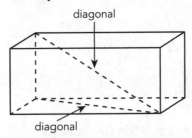

diagonal of a square

A diagonal of a square is a line segment connecting opposite vertices of the square.

diameter of the sphere

A segment drawn between two points on the sphere that passes through the center of the sphere is a diameter of the sphere.

Example

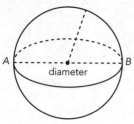

The diameter of the sphere is labeled.

dilation

A dilation is a transformation that produces a figure that is the same shape as the original figure, but not necessarily the same size.

Example

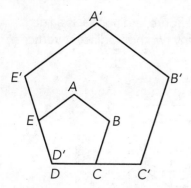

Pentagon *A'B'C'D'E'* is a dilation of Pentagon *ABCDE*.

discrete

A discrete graph is a graph of isolated points.

Examples

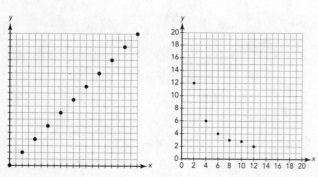

domain

The domain of a function is the set of all inputs of the function.

Example

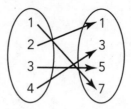

The domain in the mapping shown is {1, 2, 3, 4}.

--- E ---

ellipsis

An ellipsis is a set of three periods which stands for "and so on."

Example

3, 9, 27, 81, ...
↑
ellipsis

enlargement

When the scale factor is greater than 1, the image is called an enlargement.

explanatory variable

The independent variable can also be called the explanatory variable.

exponent

The exponent of the power is the number of times the base is used as a factor.

Examples

$2^3 = 2 \times 2 \times 2 = 8$ $8^4 = 8 \times 8 \times 8 \times 8 = 4096$
↑   ↑
exponent   exponent

exterior angle of a polygon

An exterior angle of a polygon is an angle between a side of a polygon and the extension of its adjacent side.

Example

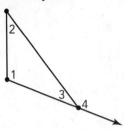

Angle 4 is an exterior angle of a polygon.

Exterior Angle Theorem

The Exterior Angle Theorem states that the measure of the exterior angle of a triangle is equal to the sum of the measures of the two remote interior angles of the triangle.

Example

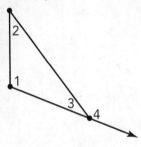

According to the Exterior Angle Theorem, $m\angle 4 = m\angle 1 + m\angle 2$.

extrapolating

Extrapolating is predicting values that fall outside the plotted values on a scatter plot.

first differences

First differences are the values determined by subtracting consecutive y-values in a table when the x-values are consecutive integers. When the first differences are equal, the points represented by the ordered pairs in the table will form a straight line.

Example

x	y
1	25
2	34
3	45

9
11

The first differences are 9 and 11, so the points represented by these ordered pairs will not form a straight line.

frequency

A frequency is the number of times an item or number occurs in a data set.

Example

Number Rolled	Tally	Frequency
2	ⵢ‖‖	7

The number 2 was rolled 7 times, so its frequency was 7.

function

A function maps each input to one and only one output.

Example

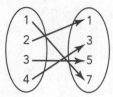

This mapping represents a function.

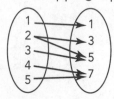

This mapping does NOT represent a function.

great circle

A great circle is the circumference of the sphere at the sphere's widest part.

Example

Point *A* is the center of the sphere. It is also the center of the great circle.

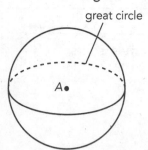

height of a cone

The height of a cone is the length of a line segment drawn from the vertex to the base of the cone. In a right cone, this line segment is perpendicular to the base.

Example

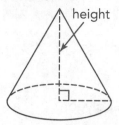

height of a cylinder

The height of a cylinder is the length of a line segment drawn from one base to the other base, perpendicular to both bases.

Example

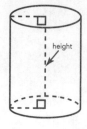

hypotenuse

The side opposite the right angle in a right triangle is called the hypotenuse.

Examples

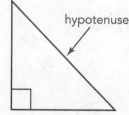
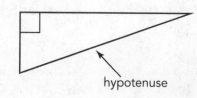

image

The new figure created from a transformation is called the image.

Example

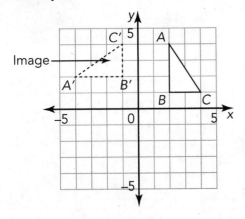

inconsistent system

Systems that have no solution are called inconsistent systems.

increasing function

When both values of a function increase together, the function is called an increasing function.

index

The index is the number placed above and to the left of the radical to indicate what root is being calculated.

Example

Index

$$\sqrt[3]{512} = 8$$

input

The first coordinate of an ordered pair in a relation is the input.

integers

Integers are the set of whole numbers and their additive inverses.

Example

The set of integers can be represented as $\{... -3, -2, -1, 0, 1, 2, 3, ...\}$

interpolating

Interpolating is predicting values that fall within the plotted values on a scatter plot.

interval of decrease

When a function is decreasing for some values of the independent variable, it is said to have an interval of decrease.

Example

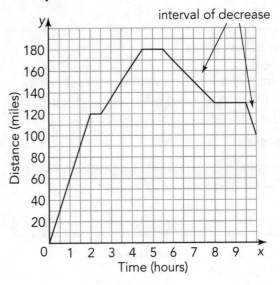

interval of increase

When a function is increasing for some values of the independent variable, it is said to have an interval of increase.

Example

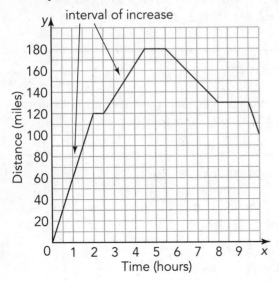

irrational numbers

Numbers that cannot be written as fractions in the form $\frac{a}{b}$, where a and b are integers and b is not equal to 0 are irrational numbers.

Examples

The numbers $\sqrt{2}$, 0.313113111..., and π are irrational numbers

---

L

---

leg

A leg of a right triangle is either of the two shorter sides. Together, the two legs form the right angle of a right triangle.

Examples

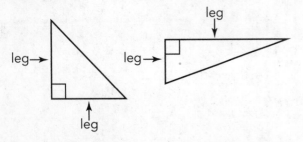

line of best fit

A line of best fit is a line that is as close to as many points as possible but doesn't have to go through all of the points.

Example

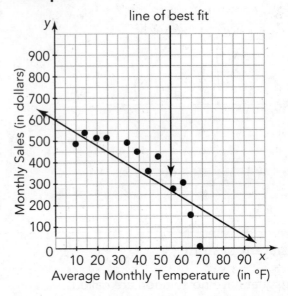

line of reflection

A line of reflection is a line that acts as a mirror so that corresponding points are the same distance from the line.

Example

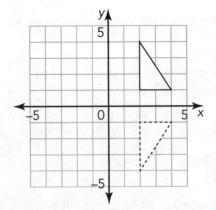

The x-axis is the line of reflection.

linear association

A linear association occurs when the points on the scatter plot seem to form a line.

Example

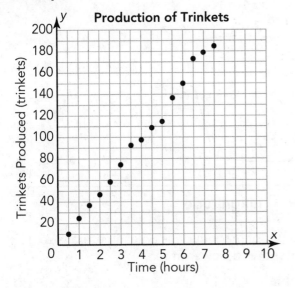

linear function

A function whose graph is a straight line is a linear function.

Example

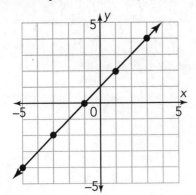

The function $f(x) = x + 1$ is a linear function.

mantissa

In the expression $a \times 10^n$, the variable a is called the mantissa. In scientific notation, the mantissa is greater than or equal to 1 and less than 10.

Example

$6.1 \times 10^5 = 610,000$

mantissa

mapping

A mapping represents two sets of objects or items. Arrows connect the items to represent a relationship between them.

Example

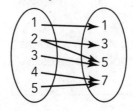

model

When you use a line of best fit, the line and its equation are often referred to as a model of the data, or a trend line. (See *trend line*.)

natural numbers

Natural numbers consist of the numbers that you use to count objects: {1, 2, 3, 4, 5, ...}

negative association

If the response variable decreases as the explanatory variable increases, then the two variables have a negative association.

Example

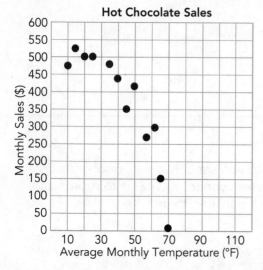

There is a negative association between average monthly temperature and hot chocolate sales.

non-linear

A non-linear graph is a graph that is not a line and therefore not a series of collinear points.

Example

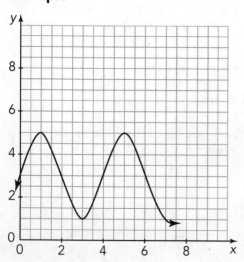

oblique cylinder

An oblique cylinder is a cylinder in which the bases are parallel to each other, but they are not aligned directly above and below each other.

Example

order of magnitude

The order of magnitude is an estimate of size expressed as a power of ten.

Example

The Earth's mass has an order of magnitude of about 10^{24} kilograms.

outlier

An outlier for bivariate data is a point that varies greatly from the overall pattern of the data.

Example

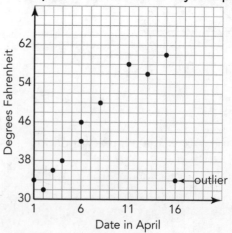

output

The second coordinate of an ordered pair in a relation is the output.

perfect cube

A perfect cube is the cube of a whole number.

Example

$4 \times 4 \times 4 = 64$ ← perfect cube

plane

A plane is a flat surface. It has infinite length and width, but no depth. A plane extends infinitely in all directions in two dimensions. Planes are determined by three points, but are usually named using one uppercase letter.

Example

Plane Q is shown.

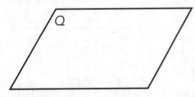

point of intersection

The point of intersection is the point at which two lines cross on a coordinate plane. In a system of linear equations, a point of intersection indicates a solution to both equations.

point-slope form

The point-slope form of a linear equation is $y - y_1 = m(x - x_1)$, where m is the slope of the line and (x_1, y_1) is any point on the line.

positive association

The two variables have a positive association if, as the explanatory variable increases, the response variable also increases.

Example

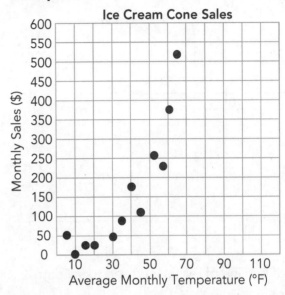

There is a positive association between the average monthly temperature and ice cream cone sales.

power

A power has two elements: the base and the exponent.

Example

base ⟶ 6^2 ← exponent
        Power

pre-image

The original figure in a transformation is called the pre-image.

Example

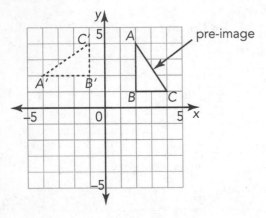

proof

A proof is a line of reasoning used to validate a theorem.

proportional relationship

A proportional relationship is one in which the ratio of the inputs to the outputs is constant. For a relationship to illustrate a proportional relationship, all the ratios $\frac{y}{x}$ or $\frac{x}{y}$, must represent the same constant.

Pythagorean Theorem

The Pythagorean Theorem states that the sum of the squares of the lengths of the legs of a right triangle equals the square of the length of the hypotenuse. If a and b are the lengths of the legs, and c is the length of the hypotenuse, then $a^2 + b^2 = c^2$.

Example

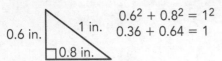

$0.6^2 + 0.8^2 = 1^2$
$0.36 + 0.64 = 1$

Pythagorean triple

Any set of three positive integers a, b, and c that satisfies the equation $a^2 + b^2 = c^2$ is a Pythagorean triple.

Example

3, 4, and 5 is a Pythagorean triple: $3^2 + 4^2 = 5^2$

Q

---

quadratic function

A quadratic function is a function that can be written in the form $y = ax^2 + bx + c$, where a, b, and c are any real numbers and a is not equal to zero.

R

---

radius of a cylinder

The radius of a cylinder is the distance from the center of the base to any point on the edge of the base.

Example

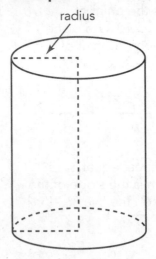

radius

radius of the sphere

A segment drawn from the center of a sphere to a point on the sphere is called a radius of the sphere.

Example

Point C is the center of the sphere, and r is the radius of the sphere.

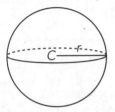

range

The range of a function is the set of all outputs of the function.

Example

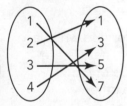

The range in the mapping shown is {1, 3, 5, 7}.

rate of change

The rate of change for a situation describes the amount that the dependent variable changes compared with the amount that the independent variable changes.

rational numbers

Rational numbers are the set of numbers that can be written as $\frac{a}{b}$, where a and b are integers and $b \neq 0$.

Examples

-4, $\frac{1}{2}$, $\frac{2}{3}$, 0.67, and $\frac{22}{7}$ are examples of rational numbers.

real numbers

Combining the set of rational numbers and the set of irrational numbers produces the set of real numbers. Real numbers can be represented on the real number line.

Examples

The numbers -3, 1.25, $\frac{11}{4}$, and $\sqrt{13}$ shown are real numbers.

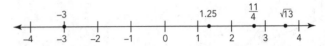

reduction

When the scale factor is less than 1, the image is called a reduction.

reflection

A reflection is a rigid motion transformation that "flips" a figure across a line of reflection.

Example

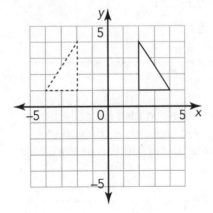

The figure has been reflected across the y-axis.

relation

A relation is any set of ordered pairs or the mapping between a set of inputs and a set of outputs.

relative frequency

A relative frequency is the ratio or percent of occurrences within a category to the total of the category.

remote interior angles of a triangle

The remote interior angles of a triangle are the two angles that are non-adjacent to the specified exterior angle.

Example

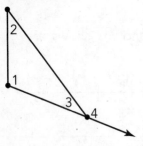

Angles 1 and 2 are remote interior angles of a triangle.

repeating decimal

A repeating decimal is a decimal in which a digit, or a group of digits, repeat(s) infinitely. Repeating decimals are rational numbers.

Examples

$\frac{1}{9} = 0.111...$ $\frac{7}{12} = 0.58333...$

$\frac{22}{7} = 3.142857142857...$

response variable

The dependent variable can also be called the response variable, because this is the variable that responds to what occurs to the explanatory variable.

right cylinder

A right cylinder is a cylinder in which the bases are aligned one directly above the other.

Example

rigid motion

A rigid motion is a special type of transformation that preserves the size and shape of the figure.

Examples

Translations, reflections, and rotations are examples of rigid motion transformations.

rotation

A rotation is a rigid motion transformation that turns a figure on a plane about a fixed point, called the center of rotation, through a given angle, called the angle of rotation.

— S —

same-side exterior angles

Same-side interior angles are formed when a transversal intersects two other lines. These angle pairs are on the same side of the transversal and are outside the other two lines.

Example

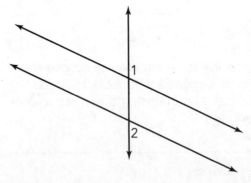

Angles 1 and 2 are same-side exterior angles.

same-side interior angles

Same-side interior angles are formed when a transversal intersects two other lines. These angle pairs are on the same side of the transversal and are between the other two lines.

Example

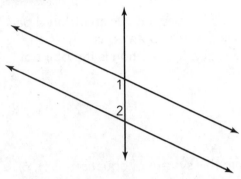

Angles 1 and 2 are same-side interior angles.

scale factor

In a dilation, the scale factor is the ratio of the distance of the new figure from the center of dilation to the distance of the original figure from the center of dilation.

Example

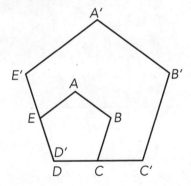

Pentagon ABCDE has been dilated by a scale factor of 2 to create Pentagon A'B'C'D'E'.

scatter plot

A scatter plot is a graph of a collection of ordered pairs that allows an exploration of the relationship between the points.

Example

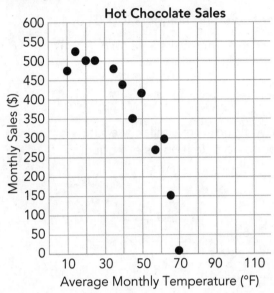

scientific notation

Scientific notation is a notation used to express a very large or a very small number as the product of a number greater than or equal to 1 and less than 10 and a power of 10.

Example

The number 1,345,000,000 is written in scientific notation as 1.345×10^9.

sequence

A sequence is a pattern involving an ordered arrangement of numbers, geometric figures, letters, or other objects.

Examples

Sequence A:

2, 4, 6, 8, 10, 12, . . .

Sequence B:

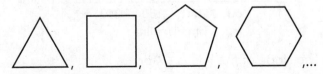

set

A set is a collection of numbers, geometric figures, letters, or other objects that have some characteristic in common.

Examples

The set of counting numbers is {1, 2, 3, 4, ...}

The set of even numbers is {2, 4, 6, 8, ...}

similar

When two figures are similar, the ratios of their corresponding side lengths are equal.

Example

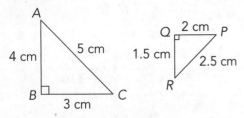

Triangle *ABC* is similar to Triangle *PQR*.

slope

In any linear relationship, slope describes the direction and steepness of a line and is usually represented by the variable *m*. Slope is another name for rate of change. (See *rate of change*.)

Example

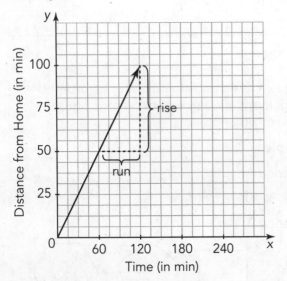

The slope of the line is $\frac{50}{60}$, or $\frac{5}{6}$.

slope-intercept form

The slope-intercept form of a linear equation is $y = mx + b$, where *m* is the slope of the line and (0, *b*) is the *y*-intercept.

solution of a linear system

The solution of a linear system is an ordered pair (*x*, *y*) that is a solution to both equations in the system. Graphically, the solution is the point of intersection.

Example

$$\begin{cases} y = x + 5 \\ y = -2x + 8 \end{cases}$$

The solution to this system of equations is (1, 6).

sphere

A sphere is the set of all points in three dimensions that are the same distance from a given point called the center of the sphere.

Example

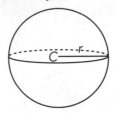

standard form

The standard form of a linear equation is $Ax + By = C$, where *A*, *B*, and *C* are constants and *A* and *B* are not both 0.

substitution method

The substitution method is a process of solving a system of equations by substituting a variable in one equation with an equivalent expression.

system of linear equations

When two or more linear equations define a relationship between quantities they form a system of linear equations.

Example

$$\begin{cases} y = x + 5 \\ y = -2x + 8 \end{cases}$$

— T —

term

A term in a sequence is an individual number, figure, or letter in the sequence.

Example

2, 7, 12, 17, 22, 27, 32, ...

term

terminating decimal

A terminating decimal has a finite number of digits, meaning that after a finite number of decimal places, all following decimal places have a value of 0. Terminating decimals are rational numbers.

Examples

$\frac{9}{10} = 0.9$ $\frac{15}{8} = 1.875$ $\frac{193}{16} = 12.0625$

transformation

A transformation is the mapping, or movement, of a plane and all the points of a figure on a plane according to a common action or operation.

Examples

Translations, reflections, rotations, and dilations are examples of transformations.

translation

A translation is a rigid motion transformation that "slides" each point of a figure the same distance and direction.

Example

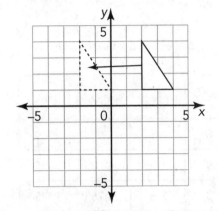

transversal

A transversal is a line that intersects two or more lines at distinct points.

Example

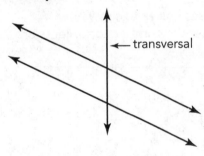

transversal

trend line

When you use a line of best fit, the line and its equation are often referred to as a model of the data, or a trend line. (See *model*.)

Triangle Sum Theorem

The Triangle Sum Theorem states that the sum of the measures of the interior angles of a triangle is 180°.

two-way table

A two-way table displays categorical data that shows the number of data points that fall into each group for two variables. One variable is divided into rows, and the other is divided into columns.

Example

Types of Snacks Purchased
Snack Types

	Popcorn	Nachos	Hot Dog	Candy
5:00 PM	200	125	75	100
7:00 PM	350	175	150	125
9:00 PM	425	225	175	125
11:00 PM	100	65	10	75

Movie Showings (row label)

---V---

Venn diagram

A Venn diagram uses circles to show how elements among sets of numbers or objects are related.

Example

Factors of 18   Factors of 30

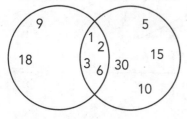

vertical line test

The vertical line test is a visual method used to determine whether a relation represented as a graph is a function. To apply the vertical line test, consider all the vertical lines that could be drawn on the graph of a relation. If any of the vertical lines intersect the graph of the relation at more than one point, then the relation is not a function.

Example

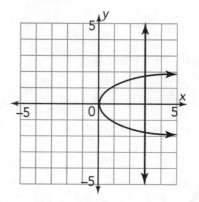

The line drawn at $x = 3$ crosses two points on the graph, so the relation is not a function.

---W---

whole numbers

Whole numbers are made up of the set of natural numbers and the number 0, the additive identity.

Example

The set of whole numbers can be represented as {0, 1, 2, 3, 4, 5, …}.

y-intercept

The y-intercept is the y-coordinate of the
point where a graph crosses the y-axis. The
y-intercept can be written in the form (0, y).

Example

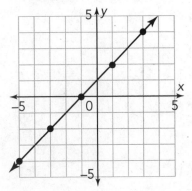

The y-intercept of the graph is (0, 1).

Index

Point of intersection (*cont.*)
  as solution of a linear
    system, M3-45
  for solving problem, M3-56
Point of rotation, M1-73, M1-
  74
Points
  collinear, M2-192
  coordinate, on graphs, M1-
    44, M1-134, M1-160
  passing through lines on
    graphs determined with
    y-intercept, M2-123
  Pythagorean Theorem used
    to determine distance
    between, M4-93–M4-95
  See also Point of
    intersection
Point-slope form, M1-137–
  M1-139
Positive associations, M2-
  276–M2-279
Postulate, M1-182
Powers
  analyzing properties, M5-
    29–M5-40
  base of, M5-9
  definition of, M5-9
  equal to 1 and numbers
    less than 1, M5-18–M5-
    21
  expanded notation and,
    M5-9, M5-14
  exponent of, M5-9–M5-10
  multiplying and dividing,
    M5-12–M5-13
  negative sign used in,
    M5-11
  of numbers in scientific
    notation, M5-46
  power to a power, M5-14–
    M5-16
  properties of, M5-7–M5-22
  quotient of, M5-17
  See also Simplifying powers
Power to a power, M5-14–
  M5-16
Power to a Power Rule
  in scientific notation, M5-78
  in simplifying powers,
    M5-22, M5-31
Pre-image, M1-20
Product Rule of Powers

in scientific notation,
  M5-63, M5-78
in simplifying powers, M5-22,
  summary of, M5-80
Proof, M4-59, M4-113
Properties
  of equality, M3-5, M3-8
  of powers, M5-7–M5-22
Properties of Equality, M3-5,
  M3-8
Pythagorean Theorem
  definition of, M4-57,
    M4-113
  distance between two
    points determined with,
    M4-93–M4-95
  introduction, M4-57–M4-58
  lengths determined with
    of diagonals in solid
      figures, M4-107–M4-108
    of diagonals in three-
      dimensional solids,
      M4-107–M4-109
    of hypotenuse, M4-57,
      M4-63–M4-66, M4-113
    of unknown side lengths
      of right triangles, M4-
      67–M4-68
  proving, M4-59–M4-62
  right triangles determined
    with, M4-57–M4-62,
    M4-113–M4-114
  studying visual proofs, M4-53
Pythagorean triple, M4-78

Q

Quadratic functions, M2-235,
  M2-260
Quantities, variable and
  constant, M2-84
Quotient Rule of Powers
  in scientific notation, M5-
    65–M5-67, M5-80
  in simplifying powers,
    M5-22, M5-31, M5-78
  summary of, M5-78

R

Radius
  of a cone, M5-100
  of a cylinder, M5-86, M5-
    89, M5-95, M5-133
  of a sphere, M5-114, M5-134

Range
  definition of, M2-208, M2-259
  of functions, M2-208,
    M2-259, M2-210
Rate of change
  calculating, from a table,
    M2-97–M2-99
  constant of proportionality
    as, M2-25–M2-27
  context used to determine,
    M2-113–M2-115
  definition of, M2-27, M2-74
  equation used to
    determine, M1-142–
    M1-143
  first differences and,
    M2-104–M2-105
  formal method for
    determining, M2-98–
    M2-99
  formula for calculating, M2-
    97–M2-99"per" used in,
    M2-113–M2-114
  rise over run ratio in, M2-153
  slope-intercept form and,
    M2-123–M2-124, M2-
    143
Rational numbers, M4-22–
  M4-23
  definition of, M4-22, M4-48
Ratios, M2-8, M2-13
Real numbers, M4-31–M4-42
Reflection, M1-53–M1-64
  definition of, M1-24
  of geometric figures on the
    coordinate plane, M1-
    53–M1-64
  on the plane, M1-22–M1-24
  over axes, 416–419
Relations
  definition of, M2-208, M2-
    259
  as functions, M2-177, M2-
    212–M2-213
  graphical representations
    of, M2-214, M2-259
  as ordered pairs, M2-207–
    M2-210
  as sequences, M2-213
Relative frequency
  of categorical data, M2-
    338, M2-341
  definition of, M2-338

rotation as, M1-27
translation as, M1-21
Translation
    definition of, M1-5, M1-21,
        M1-100
    of figures on the coordinate
        plane, M1-39–M1-49
    in line transformations,
        parallel lines related to,
        M2-76
    on plane, M1-19–M1-21
    of triangles on a coordinate
        plane, M1-92–M1-93
    verifying congruence using,
        M1-5, M1-46–M1-48,
        M1-62–M1-63
Transversal
    alternate exterior angles in,
        M1-186, M1-214
    alternate interior angles in,
        M1-186, M1-214
    angles formed by lines
        intersected by, M1-181–
        M1-196
    corresponding angles in,
        M1-185
    definition of, M1-185,
        M1-213–M1-214
    same-side exterior angles
        in, M1-186–M1-187,
        M1-214
    same-side interior angles
        in, M1-186–M1-187,
        M1-214
Trapezoids
    determining length of
        diagonals in, M4-
        101–M-105
    translating, M1-24
Trend line (model of data),
    M2-292, M2-348
Triangles
    similar
        Angle-Angle (AA) Similarity
            Theorem and, M1-205–
            M1-206, M1-215
        on the coordinate plane,
            M2-75

exploring slopes using,
    M2-43–M2-49
resulting from dilations,
    M1-144–M1-149
steepness of a line, M2-
    23–M2-38
translation of, on a
    coordinate plane, M1-
    184
See also Congruent
    triangles
Triangle Sum Theorem, M1-
    169
Two-step equations, M3-8
Two-way tables, M2-329–M2-
    340
    bivariate data displayed
        with, M2-332–M2-340
    categorical data organized
        with, M2-333
    definition of, M2-333
    frequency recorded on,
        M2-334

U

Unit rate
    definition of, M2-14
    negative, M2-34–M2-35
    rate as, M2-27, M2-30
Units of measure, comparing,
    M2-169

V

Variable quantities, M2-84
Variables, M2-272
    See also Dependent
        variables; Independent
        variables; Two-variable
        data sets
Venn diagram, M4-42–
    M4-43
Vertical angles
    description of, M1-215
    determined by two
        intersecting lines, M1-
        215
Vertical line test, M2-177,
    M2-214

Volume
    of a cone, M5-99–M5-105
    of a cylinder, M5-85–M-95
    problems, M5-123–
        M5-129
    of a sphere, M5-83,
        M5-113–M5-119

W

Whole numbers, M4-19

X

x-coordinates, M1-101, M1-
    102
x-intercepts of linear
    functions in standard
    form, M2-160–M2-161

Y

y-coordinates, M1-101, M1-
    102, M1-134
y-intercepts
    contexts used to
        determine, M2-120,
        M2-122
    definition of, M2-80, M2-
        120, M2-171
    graphs used to determine,
        M2-120, M2-173
    in lines of best fit, M2-294,
        M2-321–M2-323,
    meaning of, M2-120, M2-
        160, M2-297, M2-323
    slope-intercept form used
        to calculate, M2-121–
        M2-122, M2-123–M2-
        124
    writing, M2-164
    zero as, M2-160, M2-171

Z

Zero
    as additive identity, M4-19,
        M4-47
    on graph, axis label used to
        represent, M2-290
Zero Power Rule, M5-18, M5-
    22, M5-39, M5-78